COOKING WITH

Tanya

Quick and easy
recipes to keep
you and your
family healthy

- Tanya Rosen

Menucha Publishers, Inc.
© 2019 by Tanya Rosen

Typeset and designed by Rivkah Lewis
Food styling and photography by Chavi Feldman
Food preparation by Chaya Ruchie Schwartz

ISBN 978-1-61465-532-9

Published and distributed by:
Menucha Publishers, Inc.
1235 38th Street
Brooklyn, NY 11218
Tel/Fax: 718-232-0856
www.menuchapublishers.com
sales@menuchapublishers.com

To contact Nutrition by Tanya:
Web: www.nutritionbytanya.com
E-mail: info@nutritionbytanya.con
Tel: 844-Tanya-Diet (844-826-9234)
Instagram: @nutritionbytanya

Printed in China

Dedicated to

MY HUSBAND, WHO DOES ALL THE COOKING
(AMONGST MANY OTHER THINGS).

MY KIDS, WHO THINK I CAN'T COOK AND WHO HAVE KNOWN
WHAT A PROTEIN IS FROM THE AGE OF THREE.

MY MOM, WHO NEVER HAD TIME TO COOK MUCH BUT ROLE
MODELED HARD WORK AND SELFLESS PARENTING.

MY ENTIRE INCREDIBLE STAFF, WHO IS MY SECOND
FAMILY AND HELPED SO MUCH WITH THIS COOKBOOK,
ESPECIALLY MAYA, WHO IS THE ORGANIZATION QUEEN
AND THINKS OF EVERYTHING!

MY THREE FELLOW BOSS GIRLS, WHO MAKE EVERYTHING
HAPPEN: BASYA, RACHEL, AND ALICE.
A SPECIAL THANK YOU TO BASYA, WHO TOOK ON THIS
PROJECT WITHOUT EVEN BEING ASKED AND HEADED IT
FROM START TO FINISH.

AND LAST BUT NOT LEAST, TO THE THOUSANDS OF CLIENTS
WHO HAVE TRUSTED US WITH THEIR BODIES AND THEIR
MINDSETS, AND NOW THEIR KITCHENS TOO.

CONTENTS

DEAR READER,

Congratulations on your decision to improve or begin your healthy lifestyle by purchasing *Cooking with Tanya*. Perhaps you are already a client or you've seen our ads. Maybe you have a friend or relative who's been losing weight with our program. Maybe you noticed our logo on items such as whole wheat wraps, low-calorie ice cream, snack bags, and protein bars, endorsing these products, or you've spotted our muffins and cookies in your local grocery store. Maybe you already follow Nutrition by Tanya on Facebook or Instagram.

Have you been wondering, *Is this all hype? Is it a fad?* What is it about Nutrition by Tanya that has people talking? Why is it that we have the motto "once a client, always a client"? Why do our clients exhibit such incredible loyalty to our system? The answer lies in my dieting philosophy. While many programs encourage you to stick to a strict and punitive eating regimen in order to lose weight quickly, my approach is the opposite.

I believe that in order for weight loss to last, it needs to be sustainable; otherwise, we go right back to what we were doing (and weighing).

So yes, we all know that eating whole grains, lean proteins, and lots of vegetables is good for our health and weight loss. But on my program, we make sure we are having fun! We make sure that the foods we're eating are normal, easily accessible, enjoyable, and satisfying, so that our clients LOVE being on the plan.

There is NO detox and there is NO yo-yoing. There IS balance, portion control, and a maximized metabolism.

Each recipe in this book is divided into portion sizes that fit for anyone who is trying to eat in a normal, balanced way AND feed the family at the same time. For example, a chicken dish may be written as a single serving, but you can double it or quadruple it to serve it to your family as well.

the only way to lose weight effectively and keep it off long term is to follow a system that is moderate and balanced

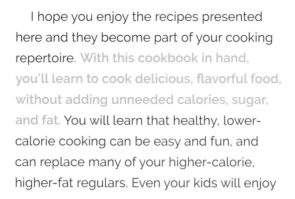

I hope you enjoy the recipes presented here and they become part of your cooking repertoire. With this cookbook in hand, you'll learn to cook delicious, flavorful food, without adding unneeded calories, sugar, and fat. You will learn that healthy, lower-calorie cooking can be easy and fun, and can replace many of your higher-calorie, higher-fat regulars. Even your kids will enjoy these recipes, and you'll set them up for a lifetime of appreciating great, healthy food, in moderation.

So once again, enjoy, and thank you for bringing me along on this journey!

Tanya

P.S. Look out for my gluten-free cookbook coming soon!

IMPORTANT TIPS

In general, we recommend using low-fat or fat-free milk whenever possible. Unsweetened almond milk is lower in calories, so if you enjoy the flavor, go ahead and use it — just be aware that the protein content in almond milk is minimal.

Many of our recipes require a sugar substitute. While the jury is still out as to which one is the healthiest, we recommend using xylitol, stevia, or Truvia. Of course, if you prefer the taste of Splenda, that is acceptable as well (ask your doctor if you are pregnant or nursing).

We recommend using whole wheat bread and whole-grain starches whenever possible. Even if the calorie count of the non–whole-grain option is similar, refined flours convert more quickly to sugar and can cause cravings and weight gain.

Fruits are not free, and not all fruits are created equal! Fruits have great health benefits, but make no mistake — they are full of carbs and can be high in calories. Having a few fruits a day can be great for your diet, but overdoing fruits can have the opposite effect.

Use cooking or baking spray instead of oil whenever possible.

We recommend lighter proteins such as milk, eggs, and yogurt for breakfast, rather than heavier proteins such as fish or chicken.

Bread, crackers, and other baked starches are best used as breakfast and lunch starches rather than for dinner, where we recommend cooked grains.

BREAKFAST

COTTAGE CHEESE SILVER-DOLLAR PANCAKES

Taking silver-dollar pancakes to a healthy level.

WHAT YOU'LL NEED

Blender or food processor
Nonstick frying pan
Spatula

YIELD

8 pancakes;
2 servings

COUNT EACH SERVING AS

1 breakfast
or 1 lunch

INGREDIENTS

1 cup reduced-fat ricotta or cottage cheese

¾ cup whole wheat flour

1 egg

2 egg whites

2 tablespoons zero-calorie sweetener

1 teaspoon kosher salt

½ teaspoon baking powder

Cooking spray

DIRECTIONS

1   Combine all ingredients except for the cooking spray in a food processor or blender. Process the mixture for about 45 seconds, pausing a couple of times to scrape the sides with a spoon or spatula until the mixture forms a thick batter.

2   Spray a pan with cooking spray and heat over medium flame. Using 2–3 tablespoons of batter per pancake, pour the batter into the hot pan in the shape of silver-dollar pancakes. Spread the batter into a thin circle after it hits the frying pan. Cook for 2–3 minutes on each side, until golden brown.

3   Test the first pancake for doneness and make sure it's cooked all the way through; if the pancakes are browning too quickly, reduce heat. Serve immediately.

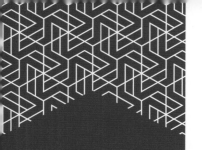

WHAT YOU'LL NEED

Blender or food processor

Nonstick frying pan

Spatula

YIELD

3–4 pancakes;
1 serving

COUNT EACH SERVING AS

1 breakfast

PROTEIN-FILLED COTTAGE CHEESE PANCAKES

Try these amazing pancakes for breakfast, or even lunch or dinner!

INGREDIENTS

½ cup reduced-fat cottage cheese

2 egg whites

¼ cup old-fashioned rolled oats or oat flour

1 teaspoon vanilla extract

1 tablespoon (15 drops) stevia or your choice of sweetener

Cooking spray

Sugar-free jelly (optional)

DIRECTIONS

1 Pour cottage cheese and egg whites into a blender or food processor, then add oats, vanilla extract, and stevia. Blend to a smooth consistency. The batter will be thin and a bit runny.

2 Spray a frying pan with cooking spray and heat pan on medium heat. Fry each pancake until golden on both sides.

3 Top with 1–2 teaspoons sugar-free jelly if desired.

OATMEAL PANCAKES

Protein-packed and delicious!

INGREDIENTS

2 packets plain instant oatmeal

4 tablespoons powdered peanut butter

4 egg whites

Zero-calorie sweetener and cinnamon, to taste

Cooking spray

DIRECTIONS

1   Mix all ingredients except for cooking spray gently with fork until fully combined.

2   Spray a frying pan with cooking spray. Heat pan and pour in ¼ of the batter at a time. Cook until lightly browned on the bottom, about 2–3 minutes, then flip and cook on the second side.

 HEALTH TIP

Why is oatmeal recommended for most meal plans?

Aside from the many health benefits it has to offer, oatmeal is full of fiber which helps keep you full for longer. It also keeps your blood sugar stable so there's no spike followed by a crash.

WHAT YOU'LL NEED

Bowl
Nonstick frying pan

YIELD

4 pancakes;
2 servings

COUNT EACH SERVING AS

1 breakfast

HEALTHY BLUEBERRY PANCAKES

Take healthy pancakes up a notch with some cottage cheese and fruit!

WHAT YOU'LL NEED

Large mixing bowl
Nonstick frying pan
Spatula

YIELD

4 servings

COUNT EACH SERVING AS

1 breakfast
or 1 lunch

INGREDIENTS

1½ cups reduced-fat cottage cheese

1 cup reduced-fat or fat-free milk

2 eggs

1 cup whole wheat flour

1 teaspoon baking powder

1 teaspoon vanilla extract

1 teaspoon cinnamon

½ cup zero-calorie sweetener

Cooking spray

1 cup blueberries (or substitute your favorite add-in)

DIRECTIONS

1 Combine all ingredients except blueberries and cooking spray in a large mixing bowl. Mix well until all ingredients are fully combined.

2 Spray a frying pan with cooking spray and heat pan over medium heat. Pour batter by the spoonful into the pan. Leave room for spreading. Immediately sprinkle a couple of blueberries onto the top of each pancake.

3 Fry until golden brown on each side, about 2–3 minutes. Serve hot with maple syrup and add more fruit if desired.

HEALTHY BANANA OMELET

Looking for a low-calorie, high-protein breakfast? Look no further...this one packs a punch!

INGREDIENTS

2 eggs or 4 egg whites

Cooking spray

1 banana, sliced

Nonfat Greek yogurt, to taste

Honey, for drizzling (optional)

DIRECTIONS

1   In a small bowl, whisk eggs or egg whites and add banana slices.

2   Spray a frying pan with cooking spray and heat. Pour batter into the frying pan. Cook as you would an omelet, flipping over when necessary.

3   When ready, remove from pan and spread Greek yogurt on top. Drizzle with honey, if desired.

WHAT YOU'LL NEED

Whisk
Small bowl
Nonstick frying pan
Spatula

YIELD

2 servings

COUNT EACH SERVING AS

1 protein

+

1 fruit

FRUITY FRENCH TOAST

Fast and easy breakfast in minutes. Perfect for the whole family!

INGREDIENTS

1 whole egg + 1 egg white

1 tablespoon reduced-fat or fat-free milk

2 slices whole wheat bread (up to 80 calories per slice)

Cooking spray

1 cup strawberries

DIRECTIONS

1   In a medium-sized bowl, whisk whole egg and egg white with milk. Soak 2 slices of whole wheat bread in the mixture.

2   Spray a pan with cooking spray and heat over medium heat. "Fry" the French toast until brown on one side. Flip over and continue cooking on the other side until brown. Serve with strawberries, if desired.

HEALTH TIP

A study conducted by scientists at the University of Tel Aviv concluded that eating a slice of bread for breakfast is less likely to make you gain weight than eating that same slice later in the day. Time your meals well in order to maximize weight loss.

WHAT YOU'LL NEED

Medium bowl

Nonstick frying pan

Whisk

Spatula

YIELD

1 serving

COUNT EACH SERVING AS

1 breakfast

+

1 fruit

FAUX-NOLA

A granola mix… without the oats! This is the perfect granola alternative!

INGREDIENTS

⅓ cup raw quinoa

½ tablespoon chia seeds

1 tablespoon honey

1 teaspoon cinnamon

2 teaspoons vanilla extract

2 tablespoons raisins

2 tablespoons whole or chopped unsalted almonds

DIRECTIONS

1 Preheat oven to 375°F.

2 Mix all the ingredients in a mixing bowl. Spread mixture onto a lined baking sheet and bake for 10–15 minutes. Using a spatula, stir the mixture every 5 minutes.

3 Once the mixture is brown, remove from oven and let cool for 10 minutes before serving.

WHAT YOU'LL NEED

Medium bowl
Baking sheet
Spatula

YIELD

3 servings

COUNT EACH SERVING AS

1 starch
(don't add a fat to this meal)

WHAT YOU'LL NEED

Small pot
Bowl

YIELD

2 servings

COUNT EACH SERVING AS

1 breakfast

+

1 fruit

CHOCOLATE-BANANA BREAKFAST QUINOA

The perfect alternative to your morning oatmeal.

INGREDIENTS

½ cup raw quinoa

1¼ cups unsweetened almond milk, divided

½ cup water

Sea salt, to taste

1 banana, divided (½ mashed, ½ sliced)

2 teaspoons honey

2 teaspoons unsweetened cocoa powder

½ teaspoon vanilla extract

Fresh mint leaves, for garnish

DIRECTIONS

1 Bring quinoa, 1 cup almond milk, water, and a dash of sea salt to a boil in a small pot. Reduce heat to a simmer and cook for about 10 minutes, stirring occasionally, until all the liquid has been absorbed. Remove from stove and transfer to a bowl.

2 Add in mashed banana, honey, cocoa powder, and vanilla. Stir until evenly combined.

3 Pour remaining ¼ cup almond milk over quinoa and garnish with banana slices and mint.

OATMEAL PEANUT BUTTER BANANA MINI MUFFINS

Packed with protein and deliciousness, these are just what you need to get a head start on your day!

INGREDIENTS

½ cup oat flour (or old-fashioned rolled oats, if using a high speed blender)

¼ cup whole wheat flour

¼ cup ground flaxseed

½ teaspoon baking soda

½ teaspoon baking powder

½ teaspoon salt

2 large very ripe bananas

¼ cup nonfat Greek yogurt

2 tablespoons reduced-fat peanut butter

2 tablespoons coconut oil

3 tablespoons honey or coconut nectar

1 egg

1 teaspoon vanilla extract

¼ cup sugar-free chocolate chips, plus a few more for sprinkling on top

¼ cup chopped almonds (optional)

DIRECTIONS

1   Preheat oven to 350°F and line a mini muffin pan with paper liners.

2   Combine all dry ingredients in a large bowl. In a smaller bowl, mash the bananas (or use a high speed blender). Add the yogurt, peanut butter, oil, honey, egg, and vanilla to the mashed bananas; blend to combine.

3   Gently stir the wet ingredients into the dry ingredients until just combined. Fold in the chocolate chips. Pour the batter into the prepared muffin pan, filling the cups only halfway. Sprinkle almonds on top, followed by some more chocolate chips. Bake for 20–25 minutes, until golden brown. Watch the muffins carefully because they bake quickly.

WHAT YOU'LL NEED

Mini muffin pan

Mini paper liners

Large bowl

Small bowl

Blender (optional)

YIELD

20 mini muffins

COUNT 1 MUFFIN AS

1 treat or 1 snack

COUNT 2 MUFFINS AS

1 breakfast

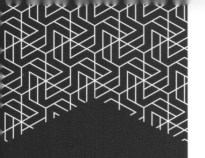

WHOLE WHEAT CHEESE BLINTZES

A breakfast or lunch that's tasty, filling, and healthy.

WHAT YOU'LL NEED

Blender or food processor

10-inch nonstick frying pan

Bowl

YIELD

10 filled crepes;
5 servings

COUNT EACH SERVING AS

1 breakfast
or 1 lunch

INGREDIENTS

CREPE BATTER

3 eggs

1 cup whole wheat flour

1 cup reduced-fat or fat-free milk

¾ cup water

1 tablespoon honey

1 teaspoon vanilla extract

¼ teaspoon salt

Cooking spray

FILLING

1 cup reduced-fat cottage cheese

4 tablespoons reduced-fat cream cheese

¼ cup zero-calorie sweetener

1 teaspoon vanilla extract

DIRECTIONS

1 Put all crepe ingredients except for cooking spray in a blender or food processor and mix well. Let stand about 15 minutes.

2 Spray a 10-inch frying pan with cooking spray and heat the pan. Pour a small amount of batter into the pan. Very quickly swirl the batter around to cover the pan in one thin layer.

3 After about 1 minute (and once it's golden brown on the bottom), carefully flip it over. Cook for 1 more minute until the other side is golden brown as well.

4 For the filling: Put the cottage cheese in a blender or food processor and process until smooth. Add cream cheese, sweetener, and vanilla. Combine until smooth.

5 Fill crepes with about 2 tablespoons of the filling and roll.

WHAT YOU'LL NEED

Blender or food processor
Bowl

YIELD

1 serving

COUNT EACH SERVING AS

1 breakfast

or omit protein scoop and count as 1 fruit + 1 snack

ACAI BOWL

Acai, pronounced "ah-si-ee," is a Brazilian berry that's captured the world. Enjoy this new favorite in a bowl.

INGREDIENTS

¾ cup frozen strawberries or raspberries

2 oz. unsweetened acai powder or ½ package Sambazon acai puree

2 tablespoons unsweetened almond milk

1 scoop of your favorite protein powder (omit if you're counting this recipe as a snack)

1 teaspoon chia seeds (for extra thickness)

TOPPINGS

1 teaspoon chopped almonds

¼ cup raspberries or blueberries

DIRECTIONS

1 Place all ingredients into a strong blender or food processor and blend briefly. Mixture should be very thick. Continue blending for several more seconds until smooth; make sure not to overblend, as this will result in a watery mixture, and you want it to be thick enough to eat with a spoon!

2 Pour into a bowl and add toppings.

SHAKSHUKA

Looking for a change? Try these poached eggs with a Middle Eastern twist.

WHAT YOU'LL NEED

Nonstick frying pan

YIELD

2 servings

COUNT EACH SERVING AS

1 protein

INGREDIENTS

Cooking spray

1 large onion, halved and thinly sliced

1 large red pepper, seeded and thinly sliced

3 cloves garlic, thinly sliced

1 teaspoon cumin

1 teaspoon paprika

⅛ teaspoon cayenne pepper, or to taste

1 28-ounce can whole plum tomatoes, coarsely chopped

¾ teaspoon salt, plus more to taste

¼ teaspoon pepper, plus more to taste

2 ounces reduced-fat feta cheese, crumbled (about 1¼ cups)

2 large eggs and 4 egg whites

Chopped cilantro, for serving

Hot sauce, for serving

DIRECTIONS

1   Preheat oven to 375˚F.

2   Spray a large frying pan with cooking spray and heat pan over medium-low heat. Add onions and red peppers. Cook gently until very soft, about 20 minutes. Add garlic and cook until tender, about 1–2 minutes. Stir in cumin, paprika, and cayenne pepper and cook 1 minute more. Pour in tomatoes and season with ¾ teaspoon salt and ¼ teaspoon pepper; simmer until tomatoes have thickened, about 10 minutes. Stir in crumbled feta.

3   Gently crack eggs into frying pan over the tomatoes. Season with salt and pepper. Transfer frying pan to oven and bake until eggs are just set, about 7–10 minutes. Sprinkle with cilantro and serve with hot sauce.

DELICIOUS ZUCCHINI QUICHE

Who would've thought you could have such a delicious quiche on a diet?

INGREDIENTS

1 white onion, diced

Cooking spray

2 zucchini, peeled and cubed

1 large red pepper, diced

1 small can sliced mushrooms, drained

1 sweet potato, sliced (optional)

4 eggs

2 tablespoons light mayonnaise

Salt and pepper, to taste

Dash each of onion powder and garlic powder

DIRECTIONS

1   Preheat oven to 350°F.

2   Sauté onion in cooking spray until golden. Add the rest of the vegetables and continue sautéing for 15 minutes. Let cool.

3   In a large bowl, whisk eggs and mayonnaise together. Add salt, pepper, onion powder, and garlic powder. Pour sautéed vegetables into egg mixture, mixing quickly so the eggs don't cook. Pour into a 9-inch round pan and bake uncovered for approximately 1 hour and 10 minutes, until top is browned.

WHAT YOU'LL NEED

Nonstick frying pan
Large bowl
Whisk
9-inch round pan

YIELD

4 servings

COUNT EACH SERVING AS

Free
or count toward your protein (if using sweet potato, count as a starch)

MINI VEGGIE QUICHES

A quick recipe that'll give you a great start to your day.

INGREDIENTS

Cooking spray

2 cups fresh spinach leaves, shredded

1 medium tomato, diced

2 cups egg whites (I like Egg Beaters)

Salt, to taste

½ teaspoon pepper

DIRECTIONS

1   Preheat oven to 350°F. Spray a muffin pan with cooking spray.

2   Divide the spinach, tomatoes, and egg whites equally among 6 muffin cups. Season with salt and pepper.

3   Bake uncovered for 15 minutes or until the whites have set. Serve hot.

WHAT YOU'LL NEED

Muffin pan

YIELD

6 mini quiches;
3 servings

COUNT EACH SERVING AS

1 protein

BAGELS

You won't believe how easy it is to make your own bagels!

INGREDIENTS

1 cup white whole wheat flour

1 cup nonfat Greek yogurt

2 teaspoons baking powder

½ teaspoon salt

Cooking spray

1 egg, beaten

Everything seasoning

DIRECTIONS

1 Preheat oven to 350°F.

2 Mix flour, yogurt, baking powder, and salt in a bowl and knead to form a dough.

3 Place parchment paper on a baking sheet and spray with cooking spray. Form dough into 4 short ropes. Form each rope into a bagel shape and attach the ends. Place them on the parchment paper and brush with beaten egg. Top with Everything seasoning.

4 Bake for 25–30 minutes until the bagels are done.

 COOKING TIP

This is a very sticky dough, so dust your hands with flour before shaping.

WHAT YOU'LL NEED

Bowl
Baking sheet
Pastry brush

YIELD

4 bagels;
½ bagel = 1 serving

COUNT EACH SERVING AS

1 bread

SALADS, DRESSINGS, AND ACCOMPANIMENTS

WHAT YOU'LL NEED

Blender or food processor

Large bowl

YIELD

4 servings

COUNT EACH SERVING AS

1 protein

+

1 fat

LETTUCE SALAD WITH AVOCADO DRESSING

Readily available and easy to prepare, avocado is a healthy fat that everyone loves.

INGREDIENTS

1 10-ounce bag cut romaine lettuce

½ red onion, sliced into rings

2 Kirby cucumbers, peeled and sliced

1¼ cups grape tomatoes, halved

4 sticks reduced-fat string cheese, sliced (optional)

Baked carrot chips (see page 43)

DRESSING

1 ripe avocado, peeled and sliced

¼ cup light mayonnaise

¼ cup water

1 teaspoon lemon juice

2 small cloves garlic, crushed

1 teaspoon salt

¼ teaspoon pepper

DIRECTIONS

1   In a large salad bowl, layer the romaine lettuce, red onions, cucumbers, and grape tomatoes.

2   Combine the dressing ingredients in a blender or food processor; blend until smooth and creamy.

3   Divide salad into 4 servings and dressing into 5 servings. Immediately before serving, pour the dressing over the salad and sprinkle with cheese if desired. Garnish with baked carrot chips. Toss gently. For a complete lunch, add whole wheat bread.

MARINATED SALAD

Does your salad look deflated? Make it marinated!

INGREDIENTS

1 red pepper, sliced

1 yellow pepper, sliced

1 zucchini, cut into matchsticks

1 carrot, cut into matchsticks

1 cup snow peas

10 green beans, halved

½ red onion, halved and sliced

DRESSING

⅓ cup balsamic vinegar

¼ cup zero-calorie sweetener

¼ teaspoon garlic powder

½ teaspoon kosher salt, or ¼ teaspoon regular salt

⅛ teaspoon pepper

DIRECTIONS

1   In a large container, combine the red and yellow peppers, zucchini, carrots, snow peas, green beans, and red onions.

2   In a small bowl, combine the dressing ingredients; whisk until blended.

3   Pour dressing over salad. Cover the container and shake to toss well.

WHAT YOU'LL NEED

Large container

Small bowl

Whisk

YIELD

4 servings

COUNT EACH SERVING AS

Free

LIGHT AND TANGY COLESLAW

You won't even miss the calories in this terrific recipe.

INGREDIENTS

1 head cabbage, finely shredded

1 small onion, minced

1 carrot, shredded

DRESSING

2 tablespoons light mayonnaise

1 tablespoon vinegar

1 tablespoon apple cider vinegar

1 tablespoon lemon juice

1 teaspoon zero-calorie sweetener

1 teaspoon salt

DIRECTIONS

1   Whisk together the dressing ingredients in a bowl and allow to stand while preparing the vegetables, about 20 minutes.

2   Pour dressing over cabbage, onion, and carrot in a large salad bowl and toss to combine. For best flavor, refrigerate slaw for at least 2 hours to overnight.

WHAT YOU'LL NEED

Bowl
Whisk

YIELD

2 servings

COUNT EACH SERVING AS

1 fat

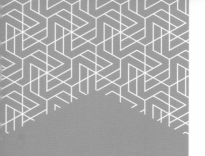

FATTOUSH SALAD

A little different from the standard, this is a perfect complement to a Middle Eastern meal.

WHAT YOU'LL NEED

Large bowl
Small bowl
Whisk

YIELD

4 servings

COUNT EACH SERVING AS

1 fat

INGREDIENTS

1 10-ounce bag cut romaine lettuce

2 Persian or Kirby cucumbers, sliced into half-moons

¼ red onion, sliced

1¼ cups grape tomatoes, halved

2 teaspoons dried parsley

1 teaspoon dried mint

Kale chips (see recipe on page 44)

DRESSING

1 teaspoon lemon juice

1 teaspoon olive oil

1 clove garlic, crushed

1¼ teaspoons kosher salt, or ¾ teaspoon regular salt

⅛ teaspoon pepper

DIRECTIONS

1   In a large salad bowl, layer the romaine lettuce, cucumbers, red onions, and grape tomatoes. Sprinkle with parsley and mint.

2   In a small bowl, whisk the dressing ingredients together. Immediately before serving, drizzle over salad and toss gently. Garnish with kale chips if desired.

Feeling uninspired? This classic, easy go-to salad will always be a hit!

WHAT YOU'LL NEED

Large salad bowl

Glass jar

YIELD

4 servings

COUNT EACH SERVING AS

1 fat

INGREDIENTS

1 10-ounce bag cut romaine lettuce or salad mix

1 Persian or Kirby cucumber, sliced into half-moons

1½ cups grape tomatoes, halved

DRESSING

¼ cup light mayonnaise

¼ cup water

2 small cloves garlic, crushed

1 teaspoon Dijon mustard

½ teaspoon salt

¼ teaspoon black pepper

DIRECTIONS

1   In a large salad bowl, layer the romaine lettuce and grape tomatoes.

2   Combine the mayonnaise, water, garlic, mustard, salt, and pepper in a glass jar. Cover and shake until smooth and creamy.

3   Immediately before serving, drizzle dressing over salad. Toss gently.

🥄 COOKING TIP

Make your salad more appealing by using the cucumber peels as garnish. Peel a cucumber before cutting it up and then arrange the peels on top of the finished salad for an eye-catching dish.

QUINOA SALAD

Incredibly refreshing and delicious, just what you need for lunch or dinner.

INGREDIENTS

2 cups cooked quinoa

2 medium Kirby cucumbers, chopped

2 cups cherry tomatoes, halved

½ red onion, finely chopped

½ avocado, chopped

2 tablespoons fresh parsley, chopped, plus more for garnish

DRESSING

6 teaspoons olive oil

⅛ cup red wine vinegar

1 teaspoon honey

1 clove garlic, minced

Kosher salt

½ teaspoon crushed red pepper flakes

1 teaspoon oregano

DIRECTIONS

1 In a large bowl, combine quinoa, cucumbers, tomatoes, onion, avocado, and parsley.

2 In a medium bowl, combine olive oil, vinegar, honey, and garlic for the dressing. Season with salt, red pepper flakes, and oregano. Whisk until combined.

3 Pour dressing over salad and toss until salad is coated in dressing. Garnish with more parsley and serve.

WHAT YOU'LL NEED

Large bowl
Medium bowl
Whisk

YIELD

4 servings

COUNT EACH SERVING AS

1 starch

+

1 fat

RADISH SALAD

Filled with fiber, potassium, and calcium, this crunchy, zingy vegetable adds a nice color and flavor contrast to your meal.

INGREDIENTS

1 cup radishes, sliced into thin discs

1 tablespoon minced red onion

1 tablespoon lemon juice

1 tablespoon balsamic vinegar

½ teaspoon Mrs. Dash

Salt and pepper, to taste

Mint leaves, fresh cilantro, or fresh parsley, for garnish

DIRECTIONS

1   Combine all ingredients, including desired amount of salt and pepper. Mix and let marinate. The longer this salad rests, the more the flavors develop, so make it a little while before you want to eat it.

2   Garnish with mint leaves, cilantro, or parsley for a fresher look and taste.

HEALTH TIP

Don't get rid of the leaves on that bunch of radishes! They're edible, delicious, and make a perfect addition to your leafy salads.

WHAT YOU'LL NEED

Small bowl

YIELD

1 serving

COUNT EACH SERVING AS

Free

JUST-RIGHT CUCUMBER SALAD

A refreshing salad that can be added to any meal.

INGREDIENTS

10 Kirby cucumbers

1–2 onions, if desired

⅓ cup zero-calorie sweetener

¼ cup lemon juice

1 tablespoon salt (less if desired)

DIRECTIONS

1   Slice cucumbers and onions as thinly as possible and place in a bowl.

2   Mix sweetener, lemon juice, and salt, and pour over cucumbers and onions. Allow salad to marinate for at least 1 hour.

WHAT YOU'LL NEED

Bowl

YIELD

4 servings

COUNT EACH SERVING AS

Free

BEET SALAD

Even your picky eaters may like beets, a healthy, filling vegetable option.

WHAT YOU'LL NEED

Whisk
Small bowl
Large bowl

YIELD

4–6 servings

COUNT EACH SERVING AS

1 starch

+

1 fat

INGREDIENTS

2 pounds cooked beets (5–6 medium beets), or 2 1-pound packages Gefen Organic Beets

1 stalk celery, finely chopped

1 large onion or shallot, finely chopped

DRESSING

2 tablespoons olive oil

2 tablespoons red wine or white wine vinegar

½ teaspoon Dijon mustard

½ teaspoon honey

½ teaspoon salt

Freshly ground pepper, to taste

DIRECTIONS

1 Whisk together dressing ingredients in a small bowl.

2 Cut beets into ½-inch cubes and place in a large bowl. Add celery, onion, and dressing; toss to coat well. Serve chilled or at room temperature.

CRUNCHY CHICKPEA CROUTONS

Chickpeas are filled with fiber and protein, while still low in calories. Great for a snack, added to a salad, or eaten as a protein.

WHAT YOU'LL NEED

Towel
Bowl
Baking pan

YIELD

15 servings

COUNT 2 TBSP AS

Free addition to soup or salad

INGREDIENTS

1 15-ounce can chickpeas, unsalted
½ teaspoon salt
2 tablespoons lemon juice
1 teaspoon lemon zest
¼–½ teaspoon black pepper

FOR RANCH-FLAVORED CHICKPEAS

1 tablespoon apple cider vinegar
½ teaspoon garlic powder
½ teaspoon onion powder
1 teaspoon dried dill
1 teaspoon dried parsley
½ teaspoon salt
¼ teaspoon black pepper

DIRECTIONS

1   Preheat oven to 400°F.

2   Drain and rinse the chickpeas. Spread onto one half of a dish towel, fold over the other half, and dry thoroughly. Remove any peels that loosened in the process. Transfer to a bowl and toss with salt, lemon juice and zest, and pepper. If desired, add vinegar and additional spices.

3   Line a baking pan with parchment paper. Spread the chickpeas evenly on the pan. Bake for 45 minutes, checking and stirring every 15 minutes for even baking. Watch them closely for the last 10 minutes, as they can burn easily.

4   Remove the pan from the oven and let the chickpeas cool for 10–15 minutes before eating. For maximum crispiness, turn off the oven, crack the door open, and let them cool in there for about 1 hour. Store in an airtight container.

BAKED CARROT CHIPS

Better than a potato chip, this is the perfect addition to a salad or just eaten alone as a side dish.

INGREDIENTS

4 small carrots

½ teaspoon kosher salt

DIRECTIONS

1   Preheat oven to 250°F.

2   Line a baking sheet with parchment paper.

3   Use a food processor or mandoline slicer to thinly slice the carrots into rounds. Arrange the carrot rounds on the baking sheet. Sprinkle with kosher salt.

4   Bake uncovered for about 45 minutes until shriveled and crispy.

WHAT YOU'LL NEED

Food processor or mandoline slicer

Baking sheet

YIELD

1 serving

COUNT EACH SERVING AS

Free

SIMPLE BAKED KALE CHIPS

Kale is a low-calorie, high-fiber, and tasty vegetable — and the perfect salad topper.

INGREDIENTS

1 cup kale, stems removed and cut into 2-inch pieces
Cooking spray, preferably olive oil flavor
Kosher salt, for sprinkling

DIRECTIONS

1   Preheat oven to 375°F.

2   Wash, check, and dry the kale leaves very well.

3   Put leaves in a bowl and spray with cooking spray. Toss to coat. Arrange kale on two lined baking sheets, making sure there is a bit of space between each leaf so that they crisp up nicely.

4   Bake uncovered for 16–18 minutes or until desired crispiness, rotating the pans halfway through.

5   Sprinkle with kosher salt and serve.

WHAT YOU'LL NEED

Medium bowl
Baking sheets

YIELD

1 serving

COUNT EACH SERVING AS

Free

TANGY BAKED KALE CHIPS

Take your kale chips up a notch with this tangy version. Makes a great snack or salad topping.

INGREDIENTS

1 cup kale, stems removed and cut into 2-inch pieces

2 tablespoons vinegar

2 tablespoons olive oil (or simply use cooking spray)

DIRECTIONS

1   Preheat oven to 350°F.

2   Wash, check, and dry the kale leaves very well.

3   Combine ingredients in a large bowl and toss to coat. Line two baking sheets with parchment paper. Spread kale on the baking sheets.

4   Bake uncovered for 10 minutes.

HEALTH TIP

Kale is one of the most nutrient-dense foods, chock full of vitamins and protein as well. These kale chips make a great salad topper!

WHAT YOU'LL NEED

Large bowl
Baking sheets

YIELD

2 servings

COUNT EACH SERVING AS

1 fat (free if using cooking spray)

HERB DRESSING

Add some zing to your salad with this simple and easy dressing.

INGREDIENTS

2–3 tablespoons apple cider vinegar

¼–½ teaspoon Mrs. Dash

DIRECTIONS

In a small bowl, combine ingredients and mix. Let sit for several minutes. Pour over salad, vegetables, or protein.

WHAT YOU'LL NEED

Small bowl

YIELD

1 serving

COUNT EACH SERVING AS

Free

ASIAN DRESSING

Put an Asian spin on your typical salad for extra yumminess.

INGREDIENTS

½ cup water

½ cup oil

1 teaspoon salt

4 tablespoons zero-calorie sweetener

1 tablespoon soy sauce

1¾ teaspoons mustard

3 teaspoons light mayonnaise

DIRECTIONS

In a small bowl, whisk together all ingredients. Pour over salad, vegetables, or protein.

WHAT YOU'LL NEED

Small bowl
Whisk

YIELD

4 servings

COUNT EACH SERVING AS

1 fat

FRENCH DRESSING

Oooh la la, c'est magnifique! Bon appetit!

INGREDIENTS

¼ teaspoon mustard

¼ cup ketchup

¼ cup vinegar

¼ cup zero-calorie sweetener, or to taste

1 clove garlic, crushed

½ teaspoon salt

¼ teaspoon paprika

¼ cup water

1 teaspoon olive oil

DIRECTIONS

Combine all ingredients in a small bowl and whisk well. Pour over salad, vegetables, or protein.

WHAT YOU'LL NEED

Small bowl

Whisk

YIELD

12 servings

COUNT EACH SERVING AS

Free

"HONEY" MUSTARD DRESSING

Great on chicken as a marinade or on the side as a dip for veggies!

INGREDIENTS

Juice of 1 lemon

1 tablespoon vinegar (any type)

1–2 cloves garlic, minced, or ½ teaspoon garlic powder

¾ teaspoon dried mustard

Salt and pepper, to taste

1 teaspoon zero-calorie sweetener

DIRECTIONS

Combine all ingredients in a small bowl. Whisk well and pour over salad, vegetables, or protein.

WHAT YOU'LL NEED

Small bowl

Whisk

YIELD

1 serving

COUNT EACH SERVING AS

Free

STRAWBERRY VINAIGRETTE DRESSING

Berry flavor with a kick of vinegar and cayenne pepper!

INGREDIENTS

2 strawberries, mashed

3 tablespoons balsamic vinegar

Salt and pepper, to taste

2 teaspoons zero-calorie sweetener

1 pinch each of cayenne pepper, onion powder, and dried mustard

1–2 cloves garlic, minced

DIRECTIONS

Place all ingredients in a bowl and mix together with a whisk. Let dressing sit for a few minutes to allow the flavors to deepen, then pour over salad, vegetables, or protein.

WHAT YOU'LL NEED

Whisk

Bowl

YIELD

1 serving

COUNT EACH SERVING AS

Free

SOUPS

VEGETABLE SOUP

A flavorful blend of ingredients, filling and just a bit different.

INGREDIENTS

Cooking spray

1 medium onion, diced

2 medium carrots, sliced

2 cloves garlic, crushed

1 14.5-ounce can diced tomatoes

3 cups water or vegetable broth

1 teaspoon dried ground thyme

2 bay leaves

1 cup broccoli or cauliflower florets

1 medium yellow squash, cut into ¾-inch cubes

1 medium zucchini, cut into ¾-inch cubes

Salt and pepper, to taste

DIRECTIONS

1   Spray a large pot with cooking spray and place over medium-high heat. Add onion and carrots. Cook, stirring frequently, for 4–5 minutes, or until onion is translucent. Add garlic and cook, stirring frequently, for 1 more minute.

2   Add tomatoes, water or broth, thyme, and bay leaves. Bring to a boil. Reduce heat to medium-low and cook, stirring occasionally, for 10 minutes.

3   Add broccoli or cauliflower and cook, stirring occasionally, for 5–6 minutes. Add squash and zucchini and cook, stirring occasionally, for 5–6 minutes. Season with salt and pepper to taste, and simmer for another 15 minutes.

WHAT YOU'LL NEED

Large pot

YIELD

4–6 servings

COUNT EACH SERVING AS

Free

CREAMY ZUCCHINI SOUP

Easy to assemble, warm, and filling. Perfect for those frigid winter days.

INGREDIENTS

1 onion, sliced

Cooking spray

3 large zucchini, peeled and sliced

4 large carrots, peeled and sliced

3 stalks celery, sliced

Water, to cover

4 tablespoons onion soup mix

Salt and pepper, to taste

DIRECTIONS

1   Sauté the onion in cooking spray for 3–5 minutes. Add the other vegetables and stir. Add water to cover and then add onion soup mix, salt, and pepper. Cook until vegetables are soft, about 30 minutes.

2   Remove soup from heat and blend until smooth and creamy.

WHAT YOU'LL NEED

Medium-sized pot

Immersion blender

YIELD

4 servings

COUNT EACH SERVING AS

Free

RICH AND DELICIOUS FRENCH ONION SOUP

Enjoy your French onion soup in a lower-fat version. With low-sodium soy sauce, this soup is both healthier and lower in calories.

INGREDIENTS

Cooking spray

4 sweet onions, sliced

1 tablespoon low-sodium soy sauce

1 tablespoon balsamic vinegar

3 cloves garlic, crushed, or
3 cubes frozen garlic

2 teaspoons brown sugar Splenda
or your choice of sweetener

½ teaspoon salt, or to taste

½ teaspoon pepper, or to taste

2 tablespoons whole wheat flour

8 cups vegetable stock or water

2 tablespoons fresh thyme, or
2 cubes frozen thyme

DIRECTIONS

1 Place a large pot over medium heat and spray with cooking spray. Add onions, soy sauce, vinegar, garlic, brown sugar substitute, salt, and pepper. Cook until the onions begin to brown and caramelize, stirring occasionally (about 30 minutes — the longer, the better).

2 Stir in the flour and let cook for another 2–3 minutes.

3 Add the broth and thyme. Cook on low for at least 30 minutes or more.

 NOTE

You can add reduced-fat cheese if desired and count as your protein for the meal.

WHAT YOU'LL NEED

Large pot

YIELD

8 servings

COUNT EACH SERVING AS

Free

ROASTED CAULIFLOWER SOUP

Roast it, blend it, and enjoy the incredible roasted flavor.

INGREDIENTS

2 bulbs garlic

½ teaspoon olive oil

2 small or 1 large white onion, diced

2 carrots, peeled and chopped

3½ cups water or vegetable stock, divided

1 32-ounce bag frozen cauliflower

½ teaspoon thyme

½ teaspoon rosemary

Salt and pepper, to taste

DIRECTIONS

1   Preheat oven to 400°F. Cut the tops off the bulbs of garlic so each clove is slightly open. Place each bulb on a small piece of aluminum foil and drizzle ¼ teaspoon olive oil over each one. Wrap in the foil and roast for 35 minutes.

2   Place the onions and carrots in a pot with some of the water or vegetable stock and cook until they start to soften, about 5–6 minutes. Add the cauliflower, the rest of the water or stock, and the thyme and rosemary. Squeeze the roasted garlic out of the bulbs and add to the pot.

3   Simmer until the cauliflower and carrots are completely soft and tender, approximately 20–25 minutes. Blend until smooth. Season with salt and pepper to taste.

WHAT YOU'LL NEED

Aluminum foil

Medium-sized pot

Immersion blender

YIELD

4 servings

COUNT EACH SERVING AS

Free

CREAMY BROCCOLI SOUP

We love any soup that needs blending! This one is so easy, you can whip it up in no time.

INGREDIENTS

1 cup broccoli

2–4 cups water, depending on desired consistency

Garlic powder, onion powder, parsley, salt, and pepper, to taste

2 tablespoons fresh parsley, finely chopped

DIRECTIONS

1 Cook broccoli in water over medium-high heat until tender, about 15 minutes. Season with garlic powder, onion powder, parsley, salt, and pepper to taste. Cook for an additional 5 minutes.

2 Using an immersion blender, blend soup to desired consistency. Garnish with fresh parsley.

WHAT YOU'LL NEED

Small pot
Immersion blender

YIELD

2 servings

COUNT EACH SERVING AS

Free

ZUCCHINI CAULIFLOWER SOUP

Filling, delicious, and healthy!

INGREDIENTS

Cooking spray

1 small onion, diced

5 medium zucchini, sliced

Water to cover

Salt and pepper, to taste

2 tablespoons onion soup mix

2 24-ounce bags frozen cauliflower

Tomato slices and fresh rosemary, for garnish (optional)

DIRECTIONS

1   Spray a medium-sized pot with cooking spray and sauté onion. When onion is soft, add zucchini. Cover with water. Add salt, pepper, and onion soup mix. Bring to a boil, then lower heat to a simmer. When zucchini is soft, add cauliflower and cook for 20–30 minutes. Blend.

2   If desired, add tomato slices and fresh rosemary on top for garnish.

WHAT YOU'LL NEED

Medium-sized pot
Immersion blender

YIELD

6 servings

COUNT EACH SERVING AS

Free

CREAMY CHICKEN SOUP

Just what the doctor and mama ordered!

WHAT YOU'LL NEED

Medium-sized pot
Immersion blender

YIELD

1 serving

COUNT EACH SERVING AS

1 protein

INGREDIENTS

Cooking spray

1 cup celery, chopped

3 cloves garlic

4–6 ounces chicken breast, cut into pieces

2 cups chicken broth

1 tablespoon dehydrated minced onion

½ teaspoon parsley

½ teaspoon basil

Salt and pepper, to taste

DIRECTIONS

1   Spray a medium-sized pot with cooking spray and add celery and garlic. Sauté over medium-high heat for 2–3 minutes. Add the rest of the ingredients and simmer until chicken cooks and celery becomes soft, about 20–30 minutes.

2   Using an immersion blender, blend the soup until it reaches a creamy consistency.

HEALTH TIP

While meat, poultry, and fish are an excellent source of protein, eating the same proteins daily can get boring. Give your meals variety by using different cuts of meat, different spices and sauces, and different cooking methods.

BEEF AND ASPARAGUS SOUP

Asparagus is packed with good-for-you vitamins and minerals. Add some beef for flavor and you've got your dinner made.

WHAT YOU'LL NEED

Medium-sized pot

YIELD

1 serving

COUNT EACH SERVING AS

1 protein
(and count toward your beef allowance)

INGREDIENTS

1 cup beef broth, prepared from fat-free, calorie-free bouillon

Additional water, as desired

4 ounces lean beef, cooked

1 cup asparagus, chopped

Salt and pepper, to taste

DIRECTIONS

1   Place broth and water in a pot. Bring to a boil over medium heat.

2   Add cooked beef and chopped asparagus. Season to taste. Simmer until asparagus is tender, about 15 minutes.

HEALTH TIP

One side effect of eating too much asparagus is constipation; however, as long as it's eaten in moderation, you can reap the benefits of this almost zero-calorie super food that is high in fiber and loaded with essential nutrients.

SIMPLE LENTIL SOUP

Lentils are high in fiber and protein, and they provide so many essential nutrients. They're also super filling and have a low glycemic index. Enjoy this quick-fix soup any time.

INGREDIENTS

1 tablespoon olive oil

1 onion, diced

3 cloves garlic, crushed

1 cup red lentils

1 teaspoon salt, or to taste

1 teaspoon cumin, or to taste

6–9 cups water

DIRECTIONS

1   Heat olive oil in a large pot over medium heat. Add the onion and garlic and sauté until golden.

2   Add remaining ingredients. Bring to a boil, then reduce heat and simmer for 1 hour or until the lentils are soft.

 HEALTH TIP

Lentils are part of the legume family and are packed with iron. Aside from being low in calories, they're also surprisingly high in protein.

WHAT YOU'LL NEED

Large pot

YIELD

6 servings

COUNT EACH SERVING AS

1 starch

CHICKEN AND MEAT MAINS

BALSAMIC CHICKEN WRAPS

You won't miss the bread in this wrap. Crunchy and delicious!

INGREDIENTS

4–6 ounces chicken breast, cubed

1–2 cloves garlic, crushed

1 tablespoon fresh ginger, finely grated, or 1 cube frozen ginger

3 tablespoons balsamic vinegar

¼ tablespoon onion powder

Salt and pepper, to taste

4 medium cabbage leaves, separated

DIRECTIONS

1   In a medium-sized bowl, mix together garlic, ginger, vinegar, onion powder, salt, and pepper. Toss in chicken pieces and coat. Cook chicken in a frying pan over medium heat until cooked through, about 10–12 minutes.

2   Tear up two cabbage leaves and add them to the chicken mixture. Continue cooking until cabbage is slightly softened, about 3–4 minutes. Spread the chicken mixture onto the two remaining cabbage leaves and roll into wraps. Serve immediately.

WHAT YOU'LL NEED

Medium-sized bowl

Nonstick frying pan

YIELD

1 serving

COUNT EACH SERVING AS

1 protein

OVEN-FRIED CHICKEN FINGERS

Make these for your kids too! A great alternative to store-bought chicken nuggets.

INGREDIENTS

4–6 ounces chicken breast, cut into strips

2 tablespoons water

1 tablespoon mustard

Salt and pepper, to taste

1 pinch each of paprika, cayenne pepper, garlic powder, and onion powder

1 piece grissini or melba toast

DIRECTIONS

1 Preheat oven to 350°F. Line a baking pan with parchment paper.

2 In a small bowl, mix water, mustard, and seasonings.

3 Grind grissini in a food processor or coffee grinder until it's a powder. Put grissini powder into a second small bowl. Add chicken to mustard mixture to coat. Dredge chicken in grissini powder and coat on both sides. Place in the baking pan.

4 Bake uncovered for about 20 minutes, turning halfway through. Turn oven to broil for the last 2–3 minutes of cooking for added crunch. Serve immediately.

WHAT YOU'LL NEED

Food processor or coffee grinder
2 small bowls
Baking pan

YIELD

1 serving

COUNT EACH SERVING AS

1 protein

ITALIAN BASIL CHICKEN

This recipe is restaurant quality. You'll feel like you're dining in an Italian restaurant!

INGREDIENTS

4–6 ounces chicken breast, thinly sliced

Juice of ½ lemon

Salt and pepper, to taste

½ cup tomato, chopped

1 orange, peeled and cut into small pieces

Fresh basil, chopped, to taste

DIRECTIONS

1   In a small pan, combine the lemon juice, salt, and pepper. Set over medium heat and add chicken. Stir to combine; add a bit of water if more moisture is needed. Cook for 2–3 minutes.

2   Add chopped tomato, orange, and fresh basil. Simmer on low for about 15 minutes, allowing the juices to marinate the chicken. Turn chicken halfway through to cook both sides evenly. Serve over rice or pasta, if allowed on your plan.

🍎 HEALTH TIP

Do you have a bright and warm area in your home? Consider using it to plant your own basil… or a small herb garden. It's easy to maintain, and you'll have fresh herbs right from your own mini garden.

WHAT YOU'LL NEED

Small pan

YIELD

1 serving

COUNT EACH SERVING AS

1 protein

WHAT YOU'LL NEED

Nonstick frying pan

YIELD

1 serving

COUNT EACH SERVING AS

1 protein

INDIAN CHICKEN CURRY

A hot and flavorful dish, perfect for when you need a change of pace.

INGREDIENTS

4–6 ounces chicken breast, thinly sliced

Cooking spray

½ medium onion, thinly sliced

1 pinch curry powder

1 pinch cayenne pepper

Salt, to taste

1–2 tablespoons water (optional)

DIRECTIONS

1   Spray a frying pan with cooking spray and sauté onion over medium heat until softened. Add the chicken and season with curry, cayenne pepper, and salt.

2   Cook the chicken, stirring occasionally, until cooked through, about 15 minutes. Turn once in the middle. Add water if the onions start to burn. Taste and add more seasonings, if desired.

❗ NOTE

This recipe also works with fish.

🍎 HEALTH TIP

Curry powder is a combination of spices that can help improve your digestive system and increase the good bacteria in your system. It contains a variety of vitamins and minerals and adds an absolutely delicious kick to any dish.

BAKED HONEY MUSTARD CHICKEN

When your taste buds crave some tangy sweetness.

INGREDIENTS

6 chicken breasts, 4–6 ounces each, thinly sliced

Cooking spray (optional)

Salt and pepper, to taste

½ cup honey

½ cup mustard

1 teaspoon basil

1 teaspoon paprika

½ teaspoon dried parsley

DIRECTIONS

1 Preheat oven to 350°F. Line a 9x13-inch baking dish with parchment paper or spray with cooking spray.

2 Sprinkle chicken breasts with salt and pepper to taste. Place chicken breast slices in the prepared baking dish. In a small bowl, combine the honey, mustard, basil, paprika, and parsley. Mix well. Pour half the mixture over the chicken and brush to cover.

3 Bake uncovered for 30 minutes. Turn chicken pieces over and brush with the remaining half of the honey mustard mixture. Bake for an additional 10–15 minutes, or until chicken is no longer pink and juices run clear. Let cool 10 minutes before serving.

WHAT YOU'LL NEED

9x13-inch baking dish

Small bowl

Pastry brush

YIELD

6 servings

COUNT EACH SERVING AS

1 protein

CHICKEN FAJITA ROLLS

In the mood for some Mexican food?

INGREDIENTS

2 chicken breasts, 4–6 ounces each

1 tablespoon olive oil

1 red pepper, thinly sliced

1 yellow pepper, thinly sliced

1 green pepper, thinly sliced

½ onion, thinly sliced

Cooking spray

FAJITA SPICE RUB

3 teaspoons chili powder

2 tablespoons cumin

1 tablespoon paprika

2 teaspoons salt

2 teaspoons garlic powder

1½ teaspoons pepper

DIRECTIONS

1 Heat olive oil in a frying pan. Add peppers and onions and sauté until soft, about 8 minutes.

2 Combine spice rub ingredients in a small bowl. Sprinkle 2 teaspoons of the spice rub into the pepper mixture.

3 Slice each chicken breast in half widthwise so you have 4 thin pieces of chicken. Pound each piece with a tenderizer.

4 Spread the pepper mixture evenly onto the chicken breasts. Roll up and skewer with toothpicks to hold their shape.

5 Slice the rolled chicken breasts into half-inch pieces, making sure each piece is held together with a toothpick.

6 Dip each roll into the remaining fajita spice rub.

7 Using cooking spray, "fry" each roll for about 3 minutes on each side until fully cooked.

WHAT YOU'LL NEED

Nonstick frying pan

Small bowl

Tenderizer

Toothpicks

YIELD

2 servings

COUNT EACH SERVING AS

1 protein

SHAKE 'N BAKE CHICKEN

A great starch-free alternative to the usual bread crumb coating.

WHAT YOU'LL NEED

Food processor or coffee grinder

9x13-inch baking pan

Airtight container

YIELD

4 servings

COUNT EACH SERVING AS

1 protein

INGREDIENTS

4 chicken breasts, 4–6 ounces each, thinly sliced

Cooking spray

SHAKE 'N BAKE COATING

½ cup minced dehydrated onions

¼ teaspoon coriander

¼ teaspoon thyme

¼ teaspoon red pepper flakes

⅛ teaspoon oregano

⅛ teaspoon paprika

⅛ teaspoon pepper

⅛ teaspoon salt

DIRECTIONS

1   Place all coating ingredients in a food processor or coffee grinder. Pulse into a powder. Store in an airtight container until ready to use.

2   Preheat oven to 350°F. Spray a 9x13-inch baking pan with cooking spray or line with parchment paper.

3   Transfer the coating to a ziplock bag and add the chicken. Shake until coated. Transfer the chicken pieces to the prepared baking dish and spray with cooking spray.

4   Place the pan in the oven and bake about 25–30 minutes, until done.

⬢ COOKING TIP

This coating works well on fish too.

CHICKEN SHAWARMA

Chicken made Middle Eastern style with a brilliantly bold flavor.

INGREDIENTS

8 boneless, skinless chicken thighs, 5 ounces each

¾ tablespoon cumin

¾ tablespoon turmeric

¾ tablespoon coriander

¾ tablespoon garlic powder

¾ tablespoon paprika

½ teaspoon ground cloves

½ teaspoon cayenne pepper, or more to taste

Salt, to taste

1 large onion, thinly sliced

Juice of 1 large lemon

2 tablespoons olive oil

Cooking spray

DIRECTIONS

1 In a small bowl, mix all the spices together.

2 Pat the chicken thighs dry and season with salt on both sides, then slice thinly into bite-sized pieces. Place in a large bowl. Add the spices and toss to coat.

3 Add the onion, lemon juice, and olive oil. Toss everything together again.

4 Cover and refrigerate for 3 hours or overnight. (If you don't have time, you can shorten or skip marinating time.)

5 Preheat oven to 425°F.

6 Take the chicken out of the fridge and let it sit at room temperature for a few minutes. Spray a large baking sheet with cooking spray.

7 Spread the marinated chicken mixture in a single layer on the baking sheet. Roast for 30 minutes.

WHAT YOU'LL NEED

Small bowl
Large bowl
Baking sheet

YIELD

8 servings

COUNT EACH SERVING AS

1 protein

APPLE CHICKEN SALAD

Add a crisp apple to your salad for some crunch and feel fuller for longer.

INGREDIENTS

4–6 ounces cooked chicken breast, cubed

1 whole apple, diced

2 stalks celery, diced

3 tablespoons lemon juice

⅛ teaspoon cinnamon

1 pinch nutmeg

1 pinch sea salt

1 cup shredded lettuce

DIRECTIONS

1 Combine chicken, apple, and celery in a bowl.

2 Add lemon juice, cinnamon, nutmeg, and salt. Mix well and serve over lettuce leaves. This salad keeps well in the refrigerator for 24 to 48 hours.

 HEALTH TIP

A salad doesn't have to be just vegetables. For a sweet and tangy twist, you can add some pieces of fruit to any leafy salad. Try it with some orange, grapefruit, strawberry, or pear slices. Just don't forget to count the fruit toward your daily fruit intake!

WHAT YOU'LL NEED

Medium bowl

YIELD

1 serving

COUNT EACH SERVING AS

1 protein

+

1 fruit

SWEET BASIL CHICKEN SALAD

Tangy and delicious, this salad is great as an appetizer or main dish.

INGREDIENTS

4–6 ounces chicken breast

Salt and pepper, to taste

2 tablespoons fresh basil, chopped

½ grapefruit, cut into bite-sized pieces, or ½ cup pomegranate seeds

1 cup spinach leaves

DRESSING

¼ cup vinegar

2 tablespoons Dijon mustard

2 tablespoons extra-virgin olive oil + ¼ cup water

Zest and juice of 1 lemon (about 4 tablespoons juice and 3 teaspoons zest)

1 clove garlic, finely minced, or 1 teaspoon garlic powder

1 tablespoon honey

1 teaspoon salt

¼ teaspoon black pepper

DIRECTIONS

1 Set oven to broil. Season chicken with salt and pepper. Broil 4–5 minutes per side in a broiler pan. Allow to cool and cut into bite-sized pieces.

2 Whisk together the dressing ingredients in a large bowl. Add chopped basil and toss. Add chicken, grapefruit or pomegranate, and spinach to the bowl. Toss and serve.

WHAT YOU'LL NEED

Broiler pan

Whisk

Large bowl

YIELD

1 serving

COUNT EACH SERVING AS

1 protein

+

½ fruit

Taking chicken to a whole new berry level!

INGREDIENTS

4–6 ounces chicken breast

Salt and pepper, to taste

1 cup shredded lettuce or spinach leaves

6 strawberries

Strawberry Vinaigrette Dressing (see page 50)

DIRECTIONS

1   Set oven to broil. Season chicken with salt and pepper and place into a broiler pan. Broil for 4–5 minutes per side. Allow to cool and cut into bite-sized pieces.

2   Place lettuce or spinach into a bowl. Slice the strawberries and add to the bowl along with the chicken. Drizzle with Strawberry Vinaigrette Dressing and toss until the lettuce is coated.

WHAT YOU'LL NEED

Broiler pan

Medium bowl

YIELD

1 serving

COUNT EACH SERVING AS

1 protein

+

½ fruit

WHAT YOU'LL NEED

Small saucepan

YIELD

3–4 servings

COUNT EACH SERVING AS

1 protein
(and count toward
your beef allowance)

SOUTHWESTERN CHILI

A great, simple-to-prepare supper dish.

INGREDIENTS

1 pound extra-lean ground beef

2 tablespoons minced onion

2 cloves garlic, crushed

1 cup canned chopped tomatoes,
or fresh tomatoes, chopped

½ cup water

¼ teaspoon chili powder

1 pinch each of garlic powder,
onion powder, and oregano

Cayenne pepper, to taste

Salt and pepper, to taste

Cauliflower Mashed Potatoes (see page 134)

DIRECTIONS

1   In a small saucepan, brown beef until no longer pink. Add in onions and garlic.

2   Stir in tomatoes and water. Add seasonings, salt, and pepper and simmer slowly until liquids reduce, about 30–40 minutes. Check frequently to make sure it's not burning. The longer the chili cooks, the more tender the beef and vegetables will be and the more flavorful it will become.

3   Serve over Cauliflower Mashed Potatoes for a complete meal.

BALSAMIC MUSTARD CRUSTED STEAK

Why spend money to go out when you can make gourmet steak at home?

INGREDIENTS

5 ounces beef fillet or London broil

1 teaspoon dried mustard

2 teaspoons balsamic vinegar

Salt and pepper, to taste

2 cloves garlic, crushed

DIRECTIONS

1 Set oven to broil.

2 Mix mustard, vinegar, salt, pepper, and garlic in a small bowl. Line a broiler pan with foil and place steak on top. Coat steak evenly with the seasoning mixture and let stand for 10 minutes.

3 Broil steak for approximately 3–4 minutes per side for medium rare. Let stand for 5 minutes to allow the juices to reabsorb. Slice and serve.

WHAT YOU'LL NEED

Small bowl

Broiler pan

Aluminum foil

YIELD

1 serving

COUNT EACH SERVING AS

1 protein

(and count toward your beef allowance)

BEEF AND CABBAGE STIR-FRY

A great alternative to stuffed cabbage, just with fewer pots to clean.

WHAT YOU'LL NEED

Nonstick frying pan
Heat-safe bowl

YIELD

1 serving

COUNT EACH SERVING AS

1 protein
(and count toward
your beef allowance)

INGREDIENTS

5 ounces extra-lean ground beef

1–2 cloves garlic, crushed

Cooking spray

1 cup shredded cabbage

1 teaspoon onion powder

Salt and pepper, to taste

DIRECTIONS

1   In a frying pan over medium heat, brown the beef with the crushed garlic. Set it aside in a heat-safe bowl.

2   Spray the pan with cooking spray and cook the cabbage until soft, about 3–4 minutes. Add the beef back into the pan and heat thoroughly. Season with onion powder, salt, and pepper to taste.

 COOKING TIP

This recipe freezes well and is a great make-ahead meal. Double, triple, or quadruple the recipe and freeze each serving in a separate container. Defrost in the microwave for 2–2½ minutes.

LOW-FAT BEEF AND BROCCOLI

Meat and veggies cooked to delicious perfection.

INGREDIENTS

1 pound pepper steak, very thinly sliced

3 tablespoons cornstarch, divided

3 tablespoons water, divided

1 tablespoon garlic powder

Cooking spray

4 cups broccoli florets

1 small onion, sliced

⅓ cup reduced-sodium soy sauce

1 tablespoon honey

1 teaspoon ground ginger

DIRECTIONS

1   In a bowl, combine 2 tablespoons cornstarch, 2 tablespoons water, and garlic powder. Mix well until smooth. Add beef and toss to coat.

2   In a large frying pan over low heat, stir-fry beef in cooking spray for about 45 minutes or until it reaches desired tenderness; remove and keep warm.

3   Spray the pan again. Add broccoli and onion and stir-fry for 4–5 minutes. Return beef to pan.

4   Combine soy sauce, honey, ginger, and remaining cornstarch and water until smooth; add to the pan. Cook, stirring, for 2 minutes.

5   Serve over brown rice (if allowed on your plan).

WHAT YOU'LL NEED

Bowl
Nonstick frying pan

YIELD

4 servings

COUNT EACH SERVING AS

1 protein
(and count toward your beef allowance)

KOFTA KEBABS

Another dish inspired by the Middle East. Add your approved amount of starch and veggies and enjoy!

WHAT YOU'LL NEED

Medium bowl

Skewers

Baking sheet

YIELD

4 servings

COUNT EACH SERVING AS

1 protein

(and count toward your beef allowance)

INGREDIENTS

1¼ pounds dark ground turkey or extra-lean ground beef

¼ cup grated onion

2 scallions, sliced (green parts only)

1¼ teaspoons cumin

1¼ teaspoons dried mint

1¼ teaspoons dried parsley

1 dash cinnamon

1¼ teaspoons kosher salt or ¾ teaspoon regular salt

⅛ teaspoon pepper

DIRECTIONS

1   In a medium bowl, mix all the ingredients together. Cover and refrigerate for at least 1 hour or overnight, to allow the flavors to penetrate.

2   Preheat oven to 400°F.

3   Form the beef mixture into 3-inch logs. Thread each meat log onto a skewer. Arrange the kebabs on a lined baking sheet and bake uncovered for 25 minutes.

PETITE MEATLOAF

Petite in size but big on taste!

INGREDIENTS

1 pound extra-lean ground beef

1 piece grissini or melba toast

½ tablespoon water

2–3 cloves garlic, crushed

½ tablespoon dehydrated minced onion

½ teaspoon spicy mustard

¼ teaspoon allspice

⅛ teaspoon sage

Salt and pepper, to taste

DIRECTIONS

1   Preheat oven to 350°F.

2   Using a food processor or coffee grinder, grind the grissini or melba toast into a powder.

3   Combine all the ingredients in a small bowl and form into a loaf. Place in a glass baking dish and bake uncovered for 25–30 minutes. Serve immediately.

WHAT YOU'LL NEED

Food processor or coffee grinder

Small bowl

Glass baking dish

YIELD

4 servings

COUNT EACH SERVING AS

1 protein

(and count toward your beef allowance)

ITALIAN MEATBALLS

Who doesn't love meatballs and spaghetti? Add a free veggie soup and enjoy a hearty meal.

INGREDIENTS

4–6 ounces extra-lean ground beef

1 piece grissini or melba toast

1 tablespoon water

1 teaspoon parsley

1 teaspoon onion powder

1 teaspoon basil

1 teaspoon oregano

1 teaspoon garlic powder

Salt and pepper, to taste

DIRECTIONS

1   Preheat oven to 425°F.

2   Using a food processor or coffee grinder, grind the grissini or melba toast into a powder.

3   Combine all ingredients in a small bowl. Form into 1-inch balls. Place the meatballs on a lined baking sheet and bake for 10 minutes, turning halfway through. Serve over spaghetti, if your plan allows.

WHAT
YOU'LL NEED

Food processor or coffee grinder

Small bowl

Baking sheet

YIELD

1 serving

COUNT EACH
SERVING AS

1 protein

(and count toward your beef allowance)

PAREVE
AND DAIRY
MAINS

WHAT YOU'LL NEED

Parchment paper
Small bowl
Baking pan

YIELD

1 serving

COUNT EACH SERVING AS

1 protein

LEMON-OREGANO FISH WITH ASPARAGUS

Steaming fish in parchment paper, known as "en papillote," creates a soft, melt-in-your-mouth texture with no added calories.

INGREDIENTS

5–6 ounces sole, tilapia, or flounder fillet

1 cup chopped asparagus, ends trimmed

Salt and pepper, to taste

Juice of 1 lemon

1 teaspoon fresh oregano, chopped

DIRECTIONS

1   Preheat oven to 400°F.

2   Place asparagus in the center of a large sheet of parchment paper. Sprinkle with salt and pepper. Place fish on top of asparagus.

3   In a small bowl, combine the lemon juice with the oregano. Pour over fish. Fold up the edges of the parchment paper to completely seal packet on all sides. Place in a baking pan and bake for 12–15 minutes, until fish flakes easily with a fork.

MOROCCAN SALMON

Tender salmon, bright tomatoes, and warm Moroccan spices make this a quick and healthy meal.

INGREDIENTS

5 ounces salmon fillet

Cooking spray

1 large onion, sliced

1 red pepper, sliced

1 yellow pepper, sliced

1 28-ounce can crushed tomatoes

1 16-ounce bag baby carrots, cut in rounds

Salt and pepper, to taste

Paprika, to taste

1 dash red pepper flakes

1 teaspoon garlic powder

1 teaspoon dried parsley

DIRECTIONS

1   Spray a frying pan with cooking spray. Sauté onion until soft, then add peppers. Pour in crushed tomatoes and baby carrots and mix. Season with salt, pepper, paprika, and red pepper flakes.

2   Lay the salmon over the sauce and sprinkle with garlic powder and dried parsley. Cover and let simmer until the salmon is ready, about 20 minutes.

WHAT YOU'LL NEED

Nonstick frying pan with lid

YIELD

1 serving

COUNT EACH SERVING AS

1 protein

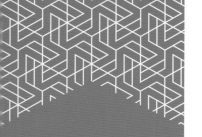

Satisfy your taste buds while keeping it clean with this Italian-infused tilapia.

WHAT YOU'LL NEED

Small bowl

Broiler pan or nonstick frying pan

YIELD

1 serving

COUNT EACH SERVING AS

1 protein

+

1 fat

INGREDIENTS

5–6 ounces tilapia fillet

1 tablespoon olive oil

2 teaspoons lemon juice

Salt and pepper, to taste

1 teaspoon oregano

Cooking spray, if pan-frying

DIRECTIONS

1   If broiling, preheat oven to broil.

2   In a small bowl, combine olive oil, lemon juice, salt, pepper, and oregano. Place tilapia in a broiler pan and pour the seasonings on top. Broil about 4 minutes, or until fish flakes easily with a fork.

3   Alternatively, heat a frying pan over medium heat and spray with cooking spray. Add the fish to the pan with the seasonings. Pan-fry about 4 minutes on each side, until browned and crispy.

 COOKING TIP

Feel free to try this dish with a different type of fish.

POKE BOWL

Hawaiian influence in a bowl full of yum!

INGREDIENTS

1 cup cooked brown rice

1 pound kani or grilled tuna steak, shredded or chopped

1 cup shelled edamame

1 medium avocado, sliced

2 Kirby cucumbers, spiralized

¼ daikon radish, spiralized

1 carrot, spiralized

2 cups sugar snap peas, cut into thin strips

2 scallions, sliced

1 teaspoon sesame seeds, toasted, for garnish

SPICY MAYONNAISE

¼ cup light mayonnaise

2 tablespoons sriracha sauce

½ teaspoon toasted sesame oil

DIRECTIONS

1 To make the spicy mayonnaise: combine all ingredients and mix until well incorporated.

2 Set out 4 bowls and place a quarter cup of cooked rice at the bottom of each bowl. Neatly divide the remaining ingredients, except for the sesame seeds, among the bowls. Drizzle a quarter of the spicy mayonnaise over the contents of each bowl. Top with toasted sesame seeds.

WHAT YOU'LL NEED

Spiralizer
Small bowl
4 serving bowls

YIELD

4 servings

COUNT EACH SERVING AS

1 lunch

or 1 dinner

(If your plan doesn't allow starch at dinner, omit the rice.)

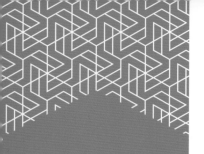

ITALIAN HERBED FISH WITH BROCCOLI

A light meal prepared in minutes. This will become your go-to fish meal.

WHAT YOU'LL NEED

Nonstick frying pan

YIELD

1 serving

COUNT EACH SERVING AS

1 protein

INGREDIENTS

5–6 ounces sole, tilapia, or flounder fillet

Salt and pepper, to taste

1 pinch each of basil, thyme, and oregano

Juice of ½ lemon

1 cup broccoli florets

1 medium tomato, peeled and diced

3 tablespoons water

Lemon wedge, for garnish

DIRECTIONS

1 Season fish with salt, pepper, and spices. Drizzle with lemon juice.

2 Heat frying pan over medium heat. Place broccoli and diced tomato with 3 tablespoons water in the frying pan and simmer until softened, about 10–12 minutes. Add fish and cook about 3–4 minutes on each side, or until fish flakes easily with a fork.

3 To serve, plate the fish and vegetables and pour pan juices on top. Garnish fish with a lemon wedge.

BROCCOLI PASTA

Your entire family can enjoy this healthy pasta recipe.

INGREDIENTS

½ cup pasta, any type

1 head broccoli, cut into florets, or 1 16-ounce bag frozen broccoli

1 teaspoon Parmesan cheese

2 ounces reduced-fat shredded mozzarella cheese

2 tablespoons marinara sauce (optional)

DIRECTIONS

1 In a small pot, cook the pasta according to package directions and drain.

2 In a separate pot, steam the broccoli until soft, about 12–14 minutes, and drain. Add the cooked pasta to the pot, along with Parmesan cheese, mozzarella, and marinara sauce, if desired. Mix over low heat until the cheese is melted.

 HEALTH TIP

Broccoli is packed with vitamins, nutrients, minerals, and so much more while still being super low in calories. It makes for a versatile and delicious addition to any healthy lifestyle.

WHAT YOU'LL NEED

Small pot
Medium-sized pot

YIELD

1 serving

COUNT EACH SERVING AS

1 complete meal

VEGGIE PASTA WITH PESTO SAUCE

Some days you just want good old comfort food. Here is a great modified version.

WHAT YOU'LL NEED

Small pot
Nonstick frying pan
Small bowl

YIELD

1 serving

COUNT EACH SERVING AS

1 starch

+

1 fat

INGREDIENTS

½ cup penne pasta

Cooking spray

1 red or yellow pepper, sliced

1 cup fresh mushrooms, sliced

1 onion, sliced

PESTO SAUCE

2 cubes frozen basil

2 cubes frozen garlic

1 tablespoon olive oil

Salt and pepper, to taste

DIRECTIONS

1 In a small pot, cook the pasta according to package directions and drain.

2 Spray a frying pan with cooking spray. Add peppers, mushrooms, and onions and sauté until soft, about 10 minutes.

3 Mix together pesto ingredients in a bowl and toss with pasta and vegetables. Serve warm.

CHEESY CAULIFLOWER BITES

A great pizza alternative!

INGREDIENTS

Cooking spray (optional)

1 32-ounce bag frozen cauliflower, defrosted

2 eggs

¾ cup reduced-fat shredded mozzarella cheese, divided

3 cubes frozen basil

1 tablespoon garlic powder

Salt and pepper, to taste

½ cup marinara sauce

DIRECTIONS

1 Preheat oven to 400°F. Line a baking sheet with parchment paper or spray with cooking spray.

2 Shred defrosted cauliflower in a food processor or with a hand grater and transfer to a large bowl.

3 Add eggs, ¼ cup mozzarella cheese, basil, and garlic powder, and season with salt and pepper. Form into small patties (they will be wet) and place on the prepared baking sheet. Bake uncovered until golden, about 20 minutes.

4 Top each patty with a thin layer of marinara sauce. Sprinkle with remaining mozzarella cheese, and bake until cheese melts, about 5–7 minutes more.

WHAT YOU'LL NEED

Baking sheet

Food processor or grater

Mixing bowl

YIELD

4–5 servings

COUNT EACH SERVING AS

1 protein

EASY-CHEESY VEGETABLE QUICHE

So easy, so cheesy, and your taste buds won't believe how yummy!

INGREDIENTS

Cooking spray

1½ cups sliced yellow squash
(2 small or 1 very large)

1½ cups sliced zucchini
(2 small or 1 very large)

1 large orange (or any color) pepper, diced

2 cloves garlic, roasted and chopped

1 tablespoon ground thyme
(or freshly chopped)

1 pinch each of salt and pepper

3 large eggs

3 large egg whites

¾ cup reduced-fat or fat-free milk

¾ teaspoon salt

¼ teaspoon freshly ground pepper

⅔ cup reduced-fat shredded cheese

DIRECTIONS

1 Heat a large frying pan over medium-high heat. Spray with cooking spray and add sliced squash and zucchini, pepper, roasted garlic, and thyme. Add a little pinch of salt and pepper. (The rest of the salt and pepper goes into the egg mixture, so just use a little pinch here.) Cook for 6–7 minutes, stirring frequently, or until vegetables are tender. Spoon into a bowl and allow to cool as you prepare the egg mixture.

2 Preheat oven to 350°F. Spray a 9-inch round pan or square pan with cooking spray. Set aside.

3 In a large bowl, whisk the eggs, egg whites, milk, salt, and pepper together until thoroughly combined.

4 Arrange cooked vegetables in the prepared pan. Top with shredded cheese, then pour the egg mixture on top.

5 Bake uncovered for 45 minutes or until filling is set. Cool for 10 minutes on a wire rack before slicing and serving.

WHAT YOU'LL NEED

Nonstick frying pan

9-inch round pan or square baking pan

Large bowl

Wire rack

YIELD

6 servings

COUNT EACH SERVING AS

1 protein

BAKED EGGPLANT PARMESAN

Eggplant is rich in dietary fiber and other nutrients, making it not only a healthy and tasty food but a filling one too.

INGREDIENTS

2 eggplants, peeled and cut into ½-inch slices

1 tablespoon salt, or as needed

1 cup Italian-style bread crumbs (whole wheat is best)

1 egg + 2 egg whites, beaten

1 28-ounce can low-sodium tomato sauce

16 ounces reduced-fat shredded mozzarella cheese

½ teaspoon basil

DIRECTIONS

1 Place eggplant slices in a strainer. Sprinkle with salt on both sides. Allow to sit for at least 3 hours. Wipe excess moisture from the eggplant slices with paper towels.

2 Preheat oven to 350°F and line a baking sheet with parchment paper.

3 Arrange beaten eggs in one bowl and bread crumbs in another. Dip eggplant slices in beaten egg, then dredge in bread crumbs. Arrange coated eggplant slices in a single layer on the prepared baking sheet. Bake for about 10 minutes, turning halfway through, until lightly browned and crisp.

4 Cover the bottom of a 9x13-inch casserole dish with a layer of tomato sauce. Top with a layer of eggplant slices and sprinkle with mozzarella cheese. Repeat layers twice, ending with a cheese layer. Sprinkle with basil.

5 Bake uncovered until cheese is bubbling and golden brown, about 35 minutes.

ZUCCHINI, ARUGULA, AND FETA FRITTATA

A healthy twist on an Italian favorite.

INGREDIENTS

1 medium zucchini

½ teaspoon sea salt + more for sprinkling

1 tablespoon olive oil

4 cups baby arugula

12 large eggs

½ cup low-fat feta cheese, crumbled

⅓ cup fresh herbs of your choice, chopped

DIRECTIONS

1 Using a grater or food processor, grate the zucchini and then place in a strainer. Sprinkle with sea salt and allow to sit for at least 1 hour (up to 3) to allow it to drain. Squeeze any remaining liquid out of the zucchini.

2 Preheat oven to 375°F. Pour the oil into a 10-inch cast-iron frying pan. Spread the oil around the full surface and sides of the frying pan (I use a paper towel). Heat the frying pan over medium heat.

3 Place the arugula in the frying pan and cover. Cook, stirring, just until wilted (about 1–2 minutes). Remove from heat and allow to cool.

4 Whisk the eggs, feta, and ½ teaspoon sea salt together in a mixing bowl. Add the zucchini, arugula, and chopped herbs. Stir together until everything is well combined. Pour the egg and vegetable mixture into the frying pan and place on the center rack of the oven.

5 Bake for 25–30 minutes or until the center has set and the top is beginning to turn golden brown. Remove from the oven and allow to sit for 10 minutes before cutting and serving.

WHAT YOU'LL NEED

Grater or food processor

Strainer

10-inch cast-iron frying pan with lid

Mixing bowl

Whisk

YIELD

6 servings

COUNT EACH SERVING AS

1 protein

(and don't add a fat to this meal)

BAKED CHEESE AND BROCCOLI PATTIES

Almost a whole meal in one! Who doesn't love gooey, cheesy patties?

WHAT YOU'LL NEED

Baking sheet

Small nonstick frying pan

Kitchen towel or cheesecloth

Large bowl

Aluminum foil

YIELD

8 patties
(3 patties = 1 serving)

COUNT EACH SERVING AS

1 protein

+

1 starch

INGREDIENTS

Cooking spray

1 tablespoon oil

2 cloves garlic, minced

½ onion, chopped

Salt and pepper, to taste

1 12-ounce bag frozen chopped broccoli, defrosted

¾ cup whole wheat panko crumbs

½ cup shredded cheddar cheese

⅓ cup Parmesan cheese

2 eggs, beaten

DIRECTIONS

1   Preheat oven to 400°F. Line a baking sheet with aluminum foil and spray lightly with cooking spray.

2   Heat the oil in a small pan over medium heat; add the garlic and onion. Sauté until tender and season with salt and pepper to taste. Set aside to cool.

3   Place the broccoli in a kitchen towel or cheesecloth and squeeze out the extra moisture. Place the drained broccoli in a large bowl. Add the onion and garlic and mix gently. Add the panko crumbs, cheeses, eggs, and some more salt and pepper to taste. Mix together and form into patties. Place on the prepared baking sheet and bake uncovered for 15 minutes. Flip and bake for another 15 minutes or until browned and crispy.

4   Add salad or vegetables for a complete meal.

SPAGHETTI SQUASH BITES

These delicious bites can replace heavier quiches at a brunch. You'll never miss the crust!

INGREDIENTS

1 medium spaghetti squash, halved

1 tablespoon olive oil

Kosher salt and pepper, to taste

1 teaspoon garlic powder

Cooking spray

1 cup tomato sauce

1 cup reduced-fat shredded mozzarella cheese

DIRECTIONS

1 Preheat oven to 400°F and line a medium-sized baking pan with parchment paper. Drizzle the cut sides of the squash with olive oil and season with salt and pepper. Roast for 45 minutes.

2 Reduce oven heat to 375°F.

3 Cool squash and shred into spaghetti pieces. Place in a bowl and season with salt, pepper, and garlic powder. Divide seasoned squash among 4 muffin cups or ramekins sprayed with cooking spray, pressing down on the bottoms and sides to create cups. Bake uncovered for 15 minutes.

4 Spoon pizza sauce into each cup and top with mozzarella cheese. Bake for 8–10 more minutes until cheese is melted.

WHAT YOU'LL NEED

Baking pan

Bowl

Muffin pan or ramekins

YIELD

4 servings

COUNT EACH SERVING AS

1 protein

BAKED ZOODLES

In place of your noodles, bake some terrific zoodles.

INGREDIENTS

3 zucchini, spiralized (see instructions below)

Cooking spray

1 16-ounce can tomato sauce

Salt and pepper, to taste

Basil, to taste

⅓ cup broccoli (optional)

½ cup reduced-fat shredded mozzarella cheese

Minced garlic (optional)

DIRECTIONS

1 Preheat oven to 350°F.

2 Rinse the zucchini well, pat dry, and chop off the ends. Using a spiralizer, make noodles out of all of the zucchini. (Once you get to the last 2 inches or so of the zucchini, it will be difficult to spiral, so you can either grate or finely chop the rest.)

3 Spray a 9x13-inch baking pan with cooking spray. Place the spiralized zucchini inside and mix with the tomato sauce. Add salt, pepper, and basil to taste. Top with broccoli and cheese and sprinkle with minced garlic, if desired.

4 Cover and bake for approximately 30 minutes, then uncover and bake for about 15 minutes more, until cheese is bubbling.

WHAT YOU'LL NEED

Spiralizer

9x13-inch baking pan

YIELD

2 servings

COUNT EACH SERVING AS

1 protein

MEDITERRANEAN ZOODLES

Pasta feeling heavy? Spiral your way to a tasty, healthier alternative.

INGREDIENTS

4 medium zucchini, spiralized
(see instructions on page 114)

1 cup cherry tomatoes, halved

⅔ cup artichoke hearts, halved

¼ cup pitted Kalamata olives, halved

2 tablespoons olive or grapeseed oil

½ lemon, juiced and zested

3 tablespoons fresh lemon juice

1 tablespoon vinegar

3 cloves garlic, minced

2 tablespoons fresh parsley, chopped

½ teaspoon kosher salt, or to taste

DIRECTIONS

1   Place the spiralized zucchini in a large serving bowl. Add cherry tomatoes, artichoke hearts, and Kalamata olives.

2   Whisk together the oil, lemon juice and zest, vinegar, garlic, parsley, and salt in a small bowl. Pour over the vegetables and toss everything together. Serve cold.

 COOKING TIP

To serve this dish hot, heat the oil, lemon juice and zest, vinegar, and garlic in a frying pan over a medium-high flame. Add the spiralized zucchini and cook until softened and much of the liquid has evaporated. Add the remaining ingredients and continue cooking until hot.

WHAT YOU'LL NEED

Spiralizer

Large bowl

Small bowl

Nonstick frying pan, if desired

YIELD

4 servings

COUNT EACH SERVING AS

1 fat

ENCHILADA BOATS

Bursting with flavor, this Mexican-inspired dish is a hit.

WHAT YOU'LL NEED

Baking sheet
Pastry brush

YIELD

4 servings

COUNT EACH SERVING AS

1 protein

INGREDIENTS

2 small spaghetti squash

2 teaspoons olive oil

Sprinkle of kosher salt

Pepper, to taste

1⅓ cups salsa

6–8 ounces reduced-fat shredded cheese

Chopped cilantro and scallions, for garnish

DIRECTIONS

1   Preheat oven to 400°F.

2   Cut the squash in half lengthwise. Use a spoon to scrape out the seeds. Brush the inside of the squash with olive oil and sprinkle lightly with salt and pepper. Place the squash face down on the baking sheet and roast for 45–50 minutes or until it can be easily pierced with a fork.

3   Cool the squash and use a fork to scrape the inside and loosen the strands. Spoon salsa into each squash bowl until almost full.

4   Top evenly with shredded cheese. Transfer the squash boats to the oven and bake another 15 minutes until the cheese is melted and the sauce is hot. Remove from oven, sprinkle with cilantro and scallions, and serve immediately.

EASY CHEESY NACHOS

A fun party food, now in single-serving size. They're so easy to make, your kids can join the fun too!

INGREDIENTS

1 ounce reduced-fat whole-grain tortilla chips (about 14 chips)

1½ ounces reduced-fat shredded mozzarella cheese

½ small red onion, diced

½ small red pepper, diced

¼ cup salsa

¼ cup nonfat Greek yogurt

1 tablespoon cilantro, chopped (optional)

1 teaspoon sliced black olives

2 tablespoons sliced jalapeño

DIRECTIONS

1   Place tortilla chips on a microwave-safe plate and top evenly with shredded cheese. Microwave on high for 1 minute or until cheese is melted and bubbly.

2   Top with remaining ingredients and serve immediately.

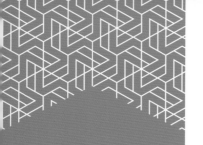

WHAT YOU'LL NEED

Microwave-safe plate

YIELD

1 serving

COUNT EACH SERVING AS

1 lunch

HOMEMADE VEGGIE BURGERS

Veggie burgers never tasted so good!

WHAT YOU'LL NEED

Grill or baking sheet
Food processor
Small and medium-sized bowls

YIELD

4 burgers;
1 burger = 1 serving

COUNT EACH SERVING AS

1 protein

INGREDIENTS

Cooking spray

1 16-ounce can black beans, drained and rinsed very well

½ green pepper

½ onion

3 cloves garlic

1 egg

1 tablespoon chili powder

1 tablespoon cumin

1 teaspoon hot sauce

2–4 tablespoons whole wheat bread crumbs

DIRECTIONS

1   If grilling, preheat an outdoor grill to high heat. Spray a sheet of aluminum foil with cooking spray.

2   If baking, preheat oven to 375°F and line a baking sheet with parchment paper.

3   In a medium bowl, mash black beans with a fork until thick and pasty. Finely chop green pepper, onion, and garlic in a food processor, then stir into the mashed beans.

4   In a small bowl, stir together egg, chili powder, cumin, and hot sauce. Stir the egg mixture into the mashed beans. Mix in bread crumbs just until the mixture is sticky and holds together. Divide the mixture into 4 patties.

5   If grilling, place patties on foil and grill about 8 minutes on each side. If baking, place patties on baking sheet and bake about 10 minutes on each side.

VEGGIE-STUFFED BAKED POTATO

Fluffiness and creaminess come together in one amazing comfort food.

INGREDIENTS

1 baked potato

¼–½ cup chopped spinach, broccoli, or mushrooms

¼ cup reduced-fat shredded mozzarella cheese

DIRECTIONS

1 Preheat oven to 400°F.

2 Halve the baked potato and scoop out the inside. Mix the potato filling with spinach, broccoli, or mushrooms, or any combination of the above. Stuff filling into potato and top with shredded mozzarella cheese. Place potato in a baking pan and cover.

3 Bake for 5–8 minutes, until cheese is melted and bubbly.

WHAT YOU'LL NEED

Baking pan

YIELD

1 serving

COUNT EACH SERVING AS

1 starch

+

1 protein

LIGHTENED-UP SIDES

BREADED SWEET POTATO WEDGES

Sweet potatoes are rich in fiber and vitamins and high in antioxidants. Add a salad to these wedges to round out your meal.

WHAT YOU'LL NEED

Baking sheet

2 bowls

Whisk

YIELD

2 servings

COUNT EACH SERVING AS

1 complete meal

INGREDIENTS

1 egg + 3 egg whites

1 medium sweet potato, cut into wedges

GARLIC PARMESAN BREADING

¼–⅓ cup whole wheat bread crumbs

2–3 tablespoons Parmesan cheese

1 tablespoon garlic powder

1 tablespoon oregano

1 teaspoon salt

¼ teaspoon pepper, or to taste

DIRECTIONS

1 Preheat oven to 375°F. Line a baking sheet with parchment paper.

2 Whisk eggs in a small bowl. Combine ingredients for breading mixture in a separate bowl.

3 Dip sweet potato wedges one at a time first in the eggs and then in the breading mixture and place on the lined baking sheet.

4 Bake uncovered for 30–35 minutes or until golden brown. For best results, turn over halfway through the baking time.

BAKED PARSNIP FRIES

The healthier version of the real thing, with less calories and fat.

INGREDIENTS

2 large parsnips, cut into fries

1 tablespoon fresh rosemary, minced

3 cloves garlic, chopped

3 tablespoons olive oil

1 dash each sea salt and pepper

½ teaspoon sweet or smoked paprika

DIRECTIONS

1   Preheat oven to 450°F. Line a baking sheet with parchment paper.

2   Peel the parsnips and trim the ends. Cut each parsnip in half horizontally and then cut each half into 9 sticks. Place in a large bowl and toss with the rosemary, garlic, oil, sea salt, pepper, and paprika.

3   Spread the fries on the baking sheet. Roast for 10 minutes, turn over, and roast for another 10–15 minutes until browned and crispy. For best results, serve with ketchup.

WHAT YOU'LL NEED

Baking sheet
Large bowl

YIELD

4 servings

COUNT EACH SERVING AS

1 fat

WHAT YOU'LL NEED

Baking sheet

Large bowl

YIELD

4 servings

COUNT EACH SERVING AS

1 fat

BAKED BROCCOLI OR CAULIFLOWER

A simple, healthy side dish, perfect for when you're short on time.

INGREDIENTS

16 ounces broccoli or cauliflower florets

2 tablespoons olive oil

3 cloves garlic, minced

½ teaspoon salt + ¼ teaspoon pepper, or ¾ teaspoon seasoned salt

⅓ cup whole wheat panko crumbs

DIRECTIONS

1   Preheat oven to 450°F. Line a baking sheet with parchment paper.

2   Mix broccoli or cauliflower with olive oil, garlic, salt, pepper, and panko crumbs. Spread mixture on the lined baking sheet.

3   Roast 13–15 minutes or until tender, stirring once.

BBQ CAULIFLOWER POPCORN

Little crispy bites of heaven. Enjoy anytime.

INGREDIENTS

1 32-ounce bag frozen cauliflower florets

1 teaspoon salt

2 teaspoons zero-calorie sweetener

¼ teaspoon onion powder

¼ teaspoon garlic powder

¼ teaspoon paprika

DIRECTIONS

1 Preheat oven to 450°F. Line a baking sheet with parchment paper.

2 Mix all the seasonings together in a large bowl. Add the cauliflower and mix well, making sure to coat it well.

3 Spread the cauliflower evenly on the lined baking sheet. Bake uncovered for 35 minutes.

WHAT YOU'LL NEED

Baking sheet
Large bowl

YIELD

4 servings

COUNT EACH SERVING AS

Free

MIDDLE EASTERN CAULIFLOWER

Za'atar is a delicious Middle Eastern spice blend of oregano, thyme, basil, and sesame seeds.

WHAT YOU'LL NEED

Baking sheet

Large bowl

YIELD

4 servings

COUNT EACH SERVING AS

Free

INGREDIENTS

24 ounces fresh cauliflower, separated into florets, or 24 ounces frozen cauliflower florets

1–2 teaspoons olive oil

1 teaspoon salt

¾–1 teaspoon cumin

1 tablespoon za'atar

DIRECTIONS

1   Preheat oven to 425°F. Line a baking sheet with parchment paper.

2   Place cauliflower pieces in a large mixing bowl. Add oil and spices and toss to combine.

3   Spread cauliflower in a single layer on the lined baking sheet. Bake uncovered for 45 minutes to an hour or until just slightly brown. Can be eaten warm or cold.

🍎 HEALTH TIP

Many fruits and vegetables contain properties that can help fight against different ailments. For example, cauliflower can protect against cancer. You'll be amazed at how much better you feel just by incorporating more veggies into your diet, regardless of your health goals.

CAULIFLOWER MASHED POTATOES

All the creamy comfort without the carbs!

INGREDIENTS

1 32-ounce bag frozen cauliflower

3 cloves garlic

1 tablespoon olive oil

½ teaspoon salt

⅛ teaspoon black pepper

DIRECTIONS

1 Bring a large pot of salted water to a boil. Add the cauliflower and garlic and cook for about 10 minutes or until the cauliflower is soft.

2 Drain and return to the pot. Let the cauliflower stand for 2–3 minutes with the lid on.

3 Transfer the cauliflower and garlic to a food processor. Add the olive oil, salt, and pepper, and puree until smooth. (You can also use a potato masher or immersion blender.) Taste and adjust the seasoning. Serve immediately.

WHAT YOU'LL NEED

Large pot

Food processor, potato masher, or immersion blender

YIELD

4 servings

COUNT EACH SERVING AS

Free

OVEN-BAKED SWEET POTATO FRIES

One potato, two potato, I'll take sweet potato fries anytime!

INGREDIENTS

2 large sweet potatoes

1 tablespoon olive oil

¼ teaspoon salt

1 teaspoon cinnamon

DIRECTIONS

1   Preheat oven to 400°F.

2   Peel sweet potatoes and cut in half lengthwise. Cut each piece into 4 wedges, then slice them down the middle. (You may also cut them into strips like regular fries.)

3   Place in a 9x13-inch baking pan and drizzle with olive oil, making sure they're evenly coated. Sprinkle with salt and cinnamon. Bake uncovered for 35 minutes, turning once in the middle.

WHAT YOU'LL NEED

9x13-inch baking pan

YIELD

2 servings

COUNT EACH SERVING AS

1 starch

+

1 fat

BALSAMIC GARLIC ASPARAGUS

You can't go wrong with such a low-calorie vegetable! It's so quick to prepare, too.

WHAT YOU'LL NEED

Large pot

YIELD

1 serving

COUNT EACH SERVING AS

Free

INGREDIENTS

1 cup asparagus spears

¼ cup balsamic vinegar

2 cloves garlic, minced

2–4 teaspoons zero-calorie sweetener

Salt and pepper, to taste

DIRECTIONS

1   Bring a pot of water to a boil. Blanch asparagus until bright green, about 3 minutes. Remove asparagus from the pot and drain the water.

2   Add vinegar, garlic, and sweetener to the pot. Cook for about 5 minutes, until the liquid is reduced. Add asparagus and toss until coated. Sprinkle with salt and pepper. Serve immediately.

🍎 HEALTH TIP

Throughout history, garlic has been used for medicinal purposes as well as for that bold flavor in cooking. It has been linked to a plethora of health benefits, including reducing blood pressure, lowering cholesterol, and helping to fight off colds.

GRILLED VEGETABLES

Grilling your veggies is a great way to jazz up any meal. Eat the rainbow!

INGREDIENTS

10 portobello mushrooms, sliced

4 large zucchini, sliced into strips

2 medium yellow peppers, sliced

2 medium orange peppers, sliced

2 medium red peppers, sliced

½ red onion, sliced

1 eggplant, sliced into strips

DRESSING

2 tablespoons olive oil

4 tablespoons balsamic vinegar

2 cloves garlic, chopped

½ teaspoon salt

Pepper, to taste

DIRECTIONS

1   Mix the dressing ingredients in a small bowl.

2   Place all the sliced vegetables in a large bowl. Pour dressing on top and mix. Grill in a grill pan or a George Foreman grill until browned.

WHAT YOU'LL NEED

Small bowl

Large bowl

Grill pan or George Foreman grill

YIELD

4 servings

COUNT EACH SERVING AS

1 fat

GARLIC STRING BEANS

A great side dish for a weeknight or Shabbos.

WHAT YOU'LL NEED

Large pot
Large bowl
Slotted spoon
Towels
Baking sheet

YIELD

4 servings

COUNT EACH SERVING AS

1 fat

INGREDIENTS

2 pounds green beans, trimmed

2 tablespoons olive oil

3 tablespoons minced garlic,
or 3 cubes frozen garlic

3 tablespoons fresh parsley, minced

2 cubes frozen dill

½ teaspoon salt

Freshly ground pepper, to taste

DIRECTIONS

1   Bring a large pot of water to a boil. Prepare a large bowl of ice water.

2   Add half the green beans to the boiling water and cook until tender-crisp, about 4 minutes. Using a slotted spoon, transfer the beans to the ice water to cool. Repeat with the remaining beans. Place a kitchen towel on a baking sheet and use a slotted spoon to transfer the beans from the ice water; blot dry with another towel.

3   Just before serving, heat oil in a large pot over medium heat. Add garlic and cook, stirring constantly, for about 30 seconds. Add the green beans and stir. Add parsley, dill, salt, and pepper. Cook, stirring, until heated through, about 1 to 3 minutes.

WHAT YOU'LL NEED

Julienne peeler

9x13-inch baking pan

Aluminum foil

YIELD

2 servings

COUNT EACH SERVING AS

1 fat

(or omit the oil and count as free)

JULIENNED VEGETABLES

It's so much fun to use a julienne peeler for a twist on veggies.

INGREDIENTS

2 large carrots, peeled

2 large zucchini, washed and unpeeled

2 medium yellow squash, washed and unpeeled

2 tablespoons olive oil

1 tablespoon kosher salt

1 teaspoon dried parsley, to taste

¼ cup boiling water

DIRECTIONS

1   Preheat oven to 400°F.

2   Using a julienne peeler, create strips of carrot, zucchini, and yellow squash. Place in a 9x13-inch baking pan. Toss with olive oil, salt, and parsley. Pour boiling water over vegetables and cover pan tightly with foil.

3   Bake for 45 minutes. Remove from oven and stir before serving.

GARLIC ROASTED VEGETABLES

This is a "clean out your fridge" type of recipe. Almost any veggie will do; the more the merrier.

INGREDIENTS

1 large zucchini, cut into half-moons

1 yellow squash, cut into half-moons

1 box mushrooms, halved

12 grape tomatoes, halved

12 baby carrots, cut in rounds

1 red onion, cut into chunks, optional

1 teaspoon olive oil

4 cloves garlic, crushed

1 tablespoon kosher salt, or 2 teaspoons regular salt

DIRECTIONS

1 Preheat oven to 400°F. Line a baking sheet with parchment paper.

2 Place all cut vegetables in a large bowl and drizzle with olive oil. Add the garlic and season with salt. Mix well. Spread vegetables in a single layer on the lined baking sheet.

3 Roast for 40 minutes.

WHAT YOU'LL NEED

Baking sheet
Large bowl

YIELD

4 servings

COUNT EACH SERVING AS

Free

YUMMY ROASTED VEGETABLES

Shake-and-bake veggies, what could be easier?

INGREDIENTS

3 zucchini, cut into chunks

3 red peppers, cut into chunks

2 onions, cut into chunks

1½ tablespoons olive oil

2 teaspoons salt

3 cloves garlic, crushed

DIRECTIONS

1   Preheat oven to 400°F. Line a baking sheet with parchment paper.

2   Place all vegetables in a large, freezer-size ziplock bag. Add olive oil, salt, and crushed garlic. Shake the bag to mix the spices and oil.

3   Spread vegetables in a single layer on the lined baking sheet and roast for 1 hour.

WHAT YOU'LL NEED

Baking sheet

Ziplock bag

YIELD

4 servings

COUNT EACH SERVING AS

1 fat

SHABBOS AND YOM TOV

WHOLE WHEAT CHALLAH

Here's a fluffy and yummy challah recipe that you can share with your loved ones at the Shabbos table.

WHAT YOU'LL NEED

Mixer or large mixing bowl

Plastic wrap

Kitchen towel

Baking sheets

Cooling rack

YIELD

48 1-ounce rolls or 5–6 large challahs

COUNT EACH SERVING AS

Your challah for the Shabbos meal

INGREDIENTS

4 packets (4 tablespoons) dry yeast

14 cups whole wheat flour

1 tablespoon salt

4 eggs

½ cup honey

½ cup oil

5 cups warm water

1 egg, beaten, for egg wash

DIRECTIONS

1 Mix all the dry ingredients together. Add eggs, honey, and oil. Slowly add the water while kneading the dough until the dough has a smooth consistency. Form a single large ball to gather the dough together.

2 Cover the bowl with a lid or plastic wrap. If using plastic wrap, cover with a towel as well. Let sit for about 1 hour or until the dough rises.

3 Preheat oven to 350˚F.

4 Line several baking sheets with parchment paper. Divide the dough into 1-ounce balls. Shape each ball into a roll and place on the baking sheet. Brush with beaten egg and bake for 15 minutes, or until golden. Set on a cooling rack to cool.

5 Alternatively, shape into 5–6 large challahs and bake for 45 minutes to an hour, until golden. (Weigh a slice before Shabbos so you'll know approximately how much an ounce of challah is.)

 NOTE

This recipe is big enough to require taking challah.

PITAS

Make your own pitas at home. Fresh and delicious! It's also another great portion-control option for Shabbos or yom tov.

INGREDIENTS

1 cup lukewarm water

1 teaspoon honey or zero-calorie sweetener

2 teaspoons dry yeast

2 cups whole wheat flour

¾ cup oat flour

1 teaspoon salt

1 tablespoon olive oil, plus more for greasing bowl

DIRECTIONS

1   In the bowl of your mixer, mix the water, honey, and yeast and let sit for about 5 minutes. Add the flours, salt, and olive oil and mix until it comes together. Knead the dough for about 5 minutes until it's smooth and elastic, adding more flour only if necessary. Form into a ball and place into a greased bowl. Cover it with a towel and allow to rest until doubled, about an hour.

2   Gently punch down the dough and turn it out onto a lightly floured work surface. Divide into 10–12 equal pieces and shape each piece into a small ball. Using a rolling pin, roll each ball into a circle about ¼ inch thick. Lift and turn the dough frequently as you roll to make sure it's not sticking to your counter. Sprinkle with a little extra flour if it starts to stick. The circles will be slightly smaller than store-bought pitas.

3   Cover the circles with plastic wrap.

4   Preheat oven to 450°F and place a baking sheet on the middle rack. When the oven is ready, transfer 3–6 pitas at a time (depending on the size of your oven) onto the baking surface and bake for 4 minutes or until the pitas balloon fully.

5   Remove the pitas from the oven and repeat with the remaining pieces of dough.

WHAT YOU'LL NEED

Mixer
Large bowl
Kitchen towel
Rolling pin
Plastic wrap
Baking sheet

YIELD

10–12 pitas

COUNT EACH PITA AS

2 breads

TOMATO DIP

Terrific as a free addition to your Shabbos or yom tov meal. Enjoy the leftover during the week too.

INGREDIENTS

1 28-ounce can whole peeled tomatoes, drained

2 10-ounce cans diced tomatoes

1 cup chopped onion

1 cup chopped red pepper

1 whole jalapeño, seeds removed, chopped

2 cloves garlic, minced

2 cubes frozen cilantro

1 whole lime, juiced

½ teaspoon salt

DIRECTIONS

Combine all ingredients in a food processor or blender until desired consistency is reached.

 HEALTH TIP

Jalapeño peppers have several health benefits. Due to a chemical called capsaicin, they can act as an anti-inflammatory, as well as help reduce headaches, clear nasal congestion, and lower blood pressure, among other things. Since they count as free on the plan, feel free to incorporate them into your other dishes as well.

WHAT YOU'LL NEED

Food processor or blender

YIELD

4 servings

COUNT EACH SERVING AS

Free

LIGHTENED-UP GUACAMOLE

Guacamole is a super-healthy food but surprisingly high in calories. Here's a way to get more bang for your buck.

WHAT YOU'LL NEED

Microwave-safe dish
Paper towel
Sieve
Large bowl

YIELD

4 servings

COUNT EACH SERVING AS

1 fat

INGREDIENTS

1 large zucchini, cut into ½-inch cubes

1 ripe avocado, cubed

2 cubes frozen cilantro, dissolved in a bit of hot water

2 cubes frozen garlic, dissolved in a bit of hot water

¼ cup finely chopped onion

2 tablespoons lemon juice

½ teaspoon hot sauce (optional)

¼ teaspoon salt

DIRECTIONS

1 Place zucchini cubes in a microwave-safe dish. Cover with a damp paper towel and microwave on high until soft, about 4–5 minutes. Drain in a sieve, pressing lightly on the zucchini to extract any liquid. Transfer to a large bowl.

2 Add avocado, cilantro, garlic, onion, lemon juice, hot sauce (if desired), and salt. Mash coarsely until combined.

SALMON IN DILL SAUCE

This simple recipe is bursting with flavor and makes for a perfect appetizer. With its nice color contrast, it looks terrific plated.

INGREDIENTS

6 salmon fillets, 4–6 ounces each

Cooking spray

½ cup light mayonnaise

¼ cup lemon juice

3 cubes frozen dill

1 teaspoon kosher salt

2 teaspoons zero-calorie sweetener

DIRECTIONS

1 Preheat oven to 425°F.

2 Place salmon in a baking pan sprayed with cooking spray.

3 In a small bowl, whisk together mayonnaise, lemon juice, dill, salt, and sweetener. Spread a thin layer of the mixture over the salmon slices. Bake uncovered for 20 minutes or until the salmon flakes easily.

WHAT YOU'LL NEED

9x13-inch baking pan

Small bowl

Whisk

YIELD

6 servings

COUNT EACH SERVING AS

1 protein

+

1 fat

WHAT
YOU'LL NEED

Small container

Baking pan

YIELD

1 serving

COUNT EACH
SERVING AS

1 protein

MEDITERRANEAN FISH

Almost any white-fleshed fish will do for this easy dinner recipe. Makes a great appetizer for a yom tov meal too.

INGREDIENTS

5–6 ounces sole, tilapia, or flounder fillet

Juice of 1 lemon, divided

2 cloves garlic, crushed

¼ teaspoon cumin

⅛ teaspoon turmeric

Salt and pepper, to taste

DIRECTIONS

1   Pour half the lemon juice into a small container and add the garlic, cumin, turmeric, salt, and pepper. Add the fish to the container and cover. Allow to marinate for up to 1 hour, refrigerated.

2   Preheat oven to 400°F.

3   Line a baking pan with parchment paper and place fish on top. Bake for 10–15 minutes, uncovered. Dress with the remaining lemon juice.

CHICKEN MARSALA

A restaurant-worthy dish, without the extra calories.

INGREDIENTS

4 chicken breasts, 4–6 ounces each

Kosher salt and pepper, to taste

¼ cup whole wheat flour

Cooking spray

2 teaspoons olive oil, divided

3 cloves garlic, crushed

¼ cup shallots, finely chopped

8 ounces cremini mushrooms, sliced

3 ounces shiitake mushrooms, sliced

⅓ cup Marsala wine

½ cup chicken broth

2 tablespoons fresh parsley, chopped, or 2 cubes frozen parsley

DIRECTIONS

1 Preheat oven to 200°F.

2 Slice the chicken breasts in half, but not all the way through, to make 4 thin cutlets. Pound cutlets lightly with a tenderizer until they are about ¼-inch thick. Season each one with ½ teaspoon kosher salt and a pinch of pepper, or to taste.

3 Put the flour in a shallow bowl and lightly dredge the chicken pieces in the flour, shaking off any excess; reserve 1 teaspoon remaining flour for later use.

4 Heat a large nonstick frying pan over medium-high heat. Spray the pan with cooking spray and add 1 teaspoon olive oil. Add the chicken and cook until slightly golden on both sides, about 3 minutes per side. Transfer to a baking dish and place in the oven to keep warm.

5 Add the remaining olive oil to the frying pan. Add the garlic and shallots and cook until soft and golden, about 2 minutes. Add the mushrooms. Season with ⅛ teaspoon kosher salt and a pinch of pepper and cook, stirring occasionally, until golden, about 5 minutes.

6 Sprinkle in the reserved 1 teaspoon of flour and cook, stirring, for about 30 seconds. Add the Marsala wine, chicken broth, and parsley. Cook, stirring and scraping up any browned bits from the bottom of the pan with a wooden spoon, until thickened, about 2 minutes.

7 Return the chicken to the frying pan, reduce heat to low, cover, and simmer in the sauce to let the flavors blend for about 4–5 minutes.

WHAT YOU'LL NEED

Tenderizer
Wax paper
Shallow bowl
Nonstick frying pan
Baking dish
Wooden spoon

YIELD

4 servings

COUNT EACH SERVING AS

1 protein
(Reduce or eliminate starch in this meal, according to your plan.)

STUFFED CHICKEN

A beautiful main dish for Shabbos or yom tov, perfect for company. Why stuff your chicken with more carbs when you can go for veggies instead?

WHAT YOU'LL NEED

Food processor

Nonstick frying pan

Tenderizer

Baking pan

Small bowl

YIELD

4 servings

COUNT EACH SERVING AS

1 protein

INGREDIENTS

4 chicken breasts, 4–6 ounces each

3 tablespoons onion soup mix

1 teaspoon salt

1 teaspoon pepper

1 teaspoon paprika

1 teaspoon garlic powder

¾ cup boiling water

VEGETABLE STUFFING

1 large zucchini

1 medium onion

1 large carrot

8–10 portobello mushrooms

Cooking spray

Salt, pepper, and garlic powder, to taste

DIRECTIONS

1 In a food processor, shred the zucchini, onion, and carrot. Slice the mushrooms thinly. Spray a large frying pan with cooking spray and sauté the shredded vegetables for 8–10 minutes. Add salt, pepper, and garlic powder to taste.

2 Preheat oven to 350°F.

3 Clean chicken breasts and pound with a tenderizer. Take a spoonful of vegetable mixture and put on the underside of the chicken. Roll up and place in a baking pan, seam side down (so it doesn't open during baking).

4 In a small bowl, combine onion soup mix, salt, pepper, paprika, garlic powder, and boiling water. Mix well until no clumps remain. Pour over stuffed chicken in pan and cover pan tightly. Bake for 1½ hours covered and then for 20 minutes uncovered.

WHAT YOU'LL NEED

Baking sheet

Bowl

Saucepan

YIELD

6 servings

COUNT EACH SERVING AS

1 protein

+

1 fruit

(and count toward your beef allowance)

MEATBALLS IN POMEGRANATE SAUCE

An elegant dish that's a perfect balance of meat with sweet.

INGREDIENTS

1 pound extra-lean ground beef

1 small onion, grated

1 clove garlic, crushed

1 tablespoon tomato paste

2 tablespoons fresh parsley, chopped

2 tablespoons whole wheat bread crumbs

1 egg

Salt and pepper, to taste

Pomegranate seeds, for garnish

POMEGRANATE SAUCE

6 cups pomegranate juice

1 cup pure maple syrup

3 tablespoons orange juice

DIRECTIONS

1   Preheat oven to 400°F. Line a baking sheet with parchment paper.

2   Combine all meatball ingredients in a bowl and mix thoroughly. Shape into 1-inch meatballs and place on the baking sheet. Bake for 20 minutes.

3   Meanwhile, prepare the pomegranate sauce: Place all ingredients in a saucepan and bring to a boil. Lower heat to medium and cook for 10 minutes, until sauce thickens slightly. Serve meatballs with pomegranate sauce and top with pomegranate seeds.

FILET MIGNON WITH ROSEMARY CABBAGE

There's nothing like a succulent steak to make dinner a hit!

WHAT YOU'LL NEED

Broiler pan
Aluminum foil
Small saucepan

YIELD

1 serving

COUNT EACH SERVING AS

1 protein
(and count toward
your beef allowance)

INGREDIENTS

4 ounces filet mignon

2 tablespoons apple cider vinegar, divided

½ teaspoon lemon pepper

1 pinch fresh or dried rosemary

1 cup shredded cabbage

3 tablespoons water

2–4 teaspoons zero-calorie sweetener

Juice of 1 lemon, to taste

DIRECTIONS

1   Preheat oven to broil.

2   Line a broiler pan with aluminum foil and place meat inside. Drizzle with 1 tablespoon vinegar and sprinkle with lemon pepper and rosemary. Broil meat for 3–4 minutes per side for medium rare. Be careful not to overcook. Allow meat to rest for 10 minutes. Slice thinly.

3   Place cabbage in a small saucepan over medium heat. Add water, remaining 1 tablespoon vinegar, and sweetener. Cook about 3–4 minutes, until cabbage softens. Place on a plate and season with as much lemon juice as desired. Arrange steak on top and enjoy.

WHAT YOU'LL NEED

Medium-sized pot

Mixing bowl

Potato masher (optional)

Nonstick frying pan

9x13-inch baking pan

YIELD

4–6 servings

COUNT EACH SERVING AS

Free (on Shabbos)

(but limit yourself to 1 serving per meal)

LIGHT SQUASH KUGEL

A healthy and filling kugel that will please the entire family! Makes for a perfect side dish for a Shabbos meal.

INGREDIENTS

6 yellow squash, peeled and cubed

2 potatoes, peeled and cubed

Cooking spray

1 onion, diced

1 8-ounce can sliced mushrooms, drained

1 teaspoon salt

2 eggs

1 teaspoon light mayonnaise

Cinnamon, to taste (optional)

DIRECTIONS

1 Place squash and potato cubes in a pot with water to cover. Bring to a boil over medium heat. Lower heat to a simmer and cook until soft, about 15–20 minutes. Drain very well. Transfer to a mixing bowl and mash with a potato masher or a fork.

2 Meanwhile, preheat oven to 350°F. Spray a 9x13-inch baking pan with cooking spray or line it with parchment paper.

3 Spray a frying pan with cooking spray and sauté the onion and mushrooms until onion is golden. Add to squash. Combine the squash mixture with the salt, eggs, and mayonnaise. Mix well.

4 Pour the mixture into the prepared pan. Sprinkle with cinnamon if desired. (For bolder flavor, sprinkle with cinnamon 1–2 minutes before removing from the oven.) Bake uncovered for 45 minutes to 1 hour, until the top is set and slightly golden.

✿ COOKING TIP

For a lighter version, leave out the potatoes and use more squash instead.

CABBAGE KUGEL

Cabbage has amazing nutritional properties. This recipe is much lighter than the traditional potato kugel. You'll love it.

INGREDIENTS

Cooking spray

1 large onion, diced

1 16-ounce bag shredded cabbage

Salt and pepper, to taste

1 tablespoon chicken soup mix

1 teaspoon garlic powder

1 teaspoon onion powder

1 egg + 2 egg whites

DIRECTIONS

1   Spray a frying pan with cooking spray and sauté the onion until soft. Add cabbage to pan and continue sautéing for approximately 45 minutes until soft. Let cool for about 15 minutes.

2   Preheat oven to 350°F. Spray a 9x13-inch baking pan or two 5x7-inch pans with cooking spray or line with parchment paper.

3   Combine the onion and cabbage mixture with the remaining ingredients in a large mixing bowl. Pour into the prepared pan or pans.

4   Bake covered for 30 minutes.

WHAT YOU'LL NEED

Nonstick frying pan

Large mixing bowl

9x13-inch baking pan or 2 5x7-inch baking pans

YIELD

4 servings

COUNT EACH SERVING AS

Free (on Shabbos) (but don't overdo your portions, as cabbage tends to bloat)

WHAT YOU'LL NEED

Mixing bowl

9x13-inch baking pan or 2 5x7-inch baking pans

YIELD

4–6 servings

COUNT EACH SERVING AS

Free (on Shabbos)

(but limit yourself to 1 serving per meal)

VEGETABLE KUGEL

A simple-to-make side dish that yields amazing results.

INGREDIENTS

Cooking spray

1 32-ounce bag frozen vegetables, defrosted

5 egg whites

2 tablespoons whole wheat flour

¼ cup light mayonnaise

1 tablespoon onion soup mix

1 8-ounce can mushrooms, drained

DIRECTIONS

1   Preheat oven to 350°F. Spray a 9x13-inch baking pan or two 5x7-inch pans with cooking spray or line with parchment paper.

2   Combine all ingredients in a bowl and mix well so the flour and soup mix don't form clumps. Pour the mixture in the prepared pan or pans. Bake uncovered for 45 minutes.

FAT-FREE BROCCOLI KUGEL

Broccoli kugel is a favorite at many Shabbos tables. Now you can enjoy it fat free.

INGREDIENTS

Cooking spray, preferably olive oil

24 ounces frozen broccoli, defrosted

6 egg whites

¼ teaspoon onion powder

¼ teaspoon garlic powder

2 teaspoons kosher salt, or 1¼ teaspoons regular salt

1 pinch pepper

DIRECTIONS

1 Preheat oven to 350°F. Spray an 8-inch square baking pan with cooking spray or line with parchment paper.

2 In a mixing bowl, chop the defrosted broccoli into smaller pieces. Lightly beat the egg whites in a second bowl and combine with the chopped broccoli. Add the onion powder, garlic powder, salt, and pepper. Mix well to combine.

3 Pour the mixture into the prepared pan. Smooth down the top with the back of a spoon. Spray with more cooking spray.

4 Bake uncovered for 1 hour.

WHAT YOU'LL NEED

8-inch baking pan

2 mixing bowls

Nonstick frying pan

YIELD

4 servings

COUNT EACH SERVING AS

Free (on Shabbos)

(use in moderation other times)

MINI APPLE MUFFINS

Who doesn't love apple muffins? These are perfect for yom tov or any special occasion.

INGREDIENTS

Cooking spray

1½ cups whole wheat pastry flour

1 teaspoon baking soda

¼ teaspoon salt

2 bananas

2 tablespoons honey

1 tablespoon vanilla extract

1 tablespoon coconut oil

1 egg

½ cup unsweetened applesauce

½ cup unsweetened apple butter

1 tablespoon unsweetened almond milk

¼ cup chopped dried apples

DIRECTIONS

1 Preheat oven to 350°F. Line 24 mini muffin cups with paper liners and lightly coat them with cooking spray.

2 In a medium bowl, whisk together the flour, baking soda, and salt.

3 Place the bananas, honey, vanilla, coconut oil, egg, almond milk, applesauce, and apple butter into a blender or food processor. Blend on high for 1 minute until well combined, smooth, and creamy.

4 Add wet mixture to dry ingredients until just combined. Do not overmix. Gently fold in apple bits.

5 Divide the batter among the prepared muffin cups. Bake for 15–20 minutes or until the tops feel firm to the touch and a toothpick inserted in the center comes out clean.

WHAT YOU'LL NEED

Mini muffin pan

Mini paper muffin liners

Mixing bowl

Whisk

Blender or food processor

YIELD

24 mini muffins; 12 servings

COUNT EACH SERVING AS

1 snack

APPLE OR BLUEBERRY COBBLER

So sweet and tasty, this is a number-one item on the menu week after week.

INGREDIENTS

¼ cup oat bran

2 tablespoons zero-calorie sweetener

1 dash cinnamon (optional)

1 cup diced apples, or 1 cup fresh blueberries

1 tablespoon water

1 drop lemon juice

DIRECTIONS

1 Preheat oven to 350°F.

2 Mix all the ingredients together in a mixing bowl. Pour into a ramekin or small baking pan and bake covered for 40 minutes, then an additional 5–10 minutes uncovered. Let cool and enjoy.

3 Alternatively, mix oat bran with cinnamon and sweetener to make a crumble. Top apples or blueberries with crumble and bake covered for 40 minutes, then an additional 5–10 minutes uncovered.

COOKING TIP

Multiply this recipe as needed so you can serve more than one person.

WHAT YOU'LL NEED

Mixing bowl

10-ounce ramekin or small baking pan

YIELD

1 serving

COUNT EACH SERVING AS

1 fruit on Shabbos

or 1 treat on other days

PUMPKIN PIE TARTLETS

Something special for Shabbos or yom tov. Skip the wonton wrappers if you prefer and enjoy a sweet side.

WHAT YOU'LL NEED

Muffin pan
Mixer

YIELD

12 tartlets

COUNT EACH SERVING AS

1 starch

(Count 1–2 tartlets as a serving, depending on your plan.)

INGREDIENTS

Cooking spray

1 15-ounce can pumpkin puree

¼ cup brown sugar Splenda or your choice of sweetener

¼ cup unsweetened almond milk

1 large egg

1½ teaspoons pumpkin pie spice

1 teaspoon ground ginger

½ teaspoon salt

24 wonton wrappers

2 tablespoons chopped pecans

DIRECTIONS

1 Preheat oven to 375°F. Spray a 12-cup muffin pan with cooking spray.

2 In the bowl of your mixer, beat together the pumpkin puree, brown sugar substitute, almond milk, egg, pumpkin pie spice, ginger, and salt.

3 Place a wonton wrapper in the bottom of each prepared muffin cup (the corners will stick up); lightly coat the wontons with cooking spray. Place a second wonton wrapper on top of the first wrapper in each cup (you can place it on an angle to make a design).

4 Divide the filling evenly among the muffin cups. Smooth the filling with the back of a spoon and sprinkle with pecans.

5 Bake until wontons are crispy and browned, about 13–17 minutes. Check the tartlets after 3–4 minutes to see if the edges are starting to burn. If they are, cover the pan loosely with aluminum foil and continue baking until the filling is set.

STRAWBERRY SORBET

Enjoy this light and refreshing recipe as a guilt-free Friday night treat.

WHAT YOU'LL NEED

Small saucepan

Blender or food processor

Ice cube trays

YIELD

6 servings

COUNT EACH SERVING AS

1 fruit

INGREDIENTS

½ cup water

1 tablespoon lemon juice

2 teaspoons vanilla extract

½ cup zero-calorie sweetener

6 cups frozen strawberries (about 2 pounds)

DIRECTIONS

1 Combine water, lemon juice, vanilla, and sweetener in a small saucepan. Heat over medium heat, stirring until sweetener has dissolved.

2 Puree the strawberries in a blender or food processor. Add the syrup and mix well. Chill the mixture in the refrigerator until cold, about 4 hours.

3 Transfer the mixture to ice cube trays and freeze until solid, about 6 hours.

4 Place frozen cubes in a blender or food processor and blend until smooth, stopping to scrape down the sides as needed. Refreeze in a container until ready to serve.

HOMEMADE VIENNESE CRUNCH

If you love dates and nuts, you'll love these delicious and easy-to-make treats.

INGREDIENTS

12 ounces dates

3 ounces almonds

3 ounces pecans

6 ounces (about ⅔ cup) reduced-fat peanut butter

DIRECTIONS

1   Blend dates in a food processor and set aside.

2   Chop almonds and pecans in the food processor, then mix with the peanut butter. Add the dates and mix well by hand.

3   Roll the mixture into 20 balls or logs. Store in a container and freeze.

 COOKING TIP

When choosing dates, select ones that don't have crystals on them. Crystallization means they're less fresh. Also, when removing the pits, sprinkle some flour on your knife to keep it from sticking.

WHAT YOU'LL NEED

Food processor

Mixing bowl

YIELD

20 servings

COUNT EACH SERVING AS

1 treat

or 1 snack

WHAT YOU'LL NEED

Blender or food processor

YIELD

35–40 balls

COUNT EACH SERVING AS

1 snack or treat

(Count 2–3 balls as a serving, depending on your plan.)

DATE AND NUT POWER BALLS

These are a great Pesach treat. You can also enjoy them on Tu B'Shvat or at any other time of year.

INGREDIENTS

1 cup raw almonds

1 cup raw cashews

2 cups dried cranberries or dried apricots

6 dates, pitted

¼ teaspoon vanilla extract

¼ cup unsweetened shredded coconut

DIRECTIONS

1 Place the almonds and cashews into a blender or food processor and pulse for a few seconds.

2 Add the dried fruit, dates, vanilla, and coconut. Pulse just until the mixture looks wet and begins to form a ball, about 30 seconds.

3 Roll into 35–40 balls and chill before serving.

HEALTH TIP

There are only a select few types of nuts that are considered on the "healthier" end of the spectrum. The best of the best are almonds, followed by cashews.

CHOCOLATE BARK

Calling all chocoholics! Come and get your chocolate fix!

WHAT YOU'LL NEED

Small saucepan

Mixing bowl

Silicone or plastic mat

YIELD

12 servings

COUNT EACH SERVING AS

1 treat

INGREDIENTS

½ cup coconut oil

5–7 tablespoons honey

1 cup unsweetened cocoa powder

1 teaspoon vanilla extract

1 tablespoon crushed almonds, cashews, or pistachios

DIRECTIONS

1   Place the coconut oil in a small saucepan and melt over low heat. Add in the honey and cocoa, mixing after each addition. Stir until the mixture is smooth and appears glossy, about 1–2 minutes. Remove from heat.

2   Pour the mixture onto a silicone or plastic mat and smooth out. Sprinkle the crushed nuts on top and freeze for a couple of minutes. Once hardened, break into pieces or clusters and separate into 12 servings. Store in a ziplock bag or container in the freezer.

 NOTE

This recipe is great for Pesach.

BAKED POTATO LATKES

Perfect for Chanukah or any occasion.

INGREDIENTS

2 pounds potatoes, shredded or grated

1 onion, shredded or grated

2 eggs

Salt and pepper, to taste

¼ cup whole wheat matzah meal
or ¼ cup whole wheat flour

¼ teaspoon baking powder

Cooking spray

DIRECTIONS

1   Preheat oven to 425°F.

2   Drain excess liquid from potatoes and onions. Mix all ingredients except for cooking spray in a large bowl.

3   Spray two baking sheets with cooking spray. Add latke mixture ¼ cup at a time and flatten for a total of 16 latkes.

4   Bake uncovered for 15 minutes. Flip latkes and bake 10 minutes longer.

WHAT YOU'LL NEED

Food processor
Large bowl
Baking sheets

YIELD

16 latkes
(1–2 latkes per serving)

COUNT EACH SERVING AS

1 starch

MINI DOUGHNUTS

Treat yourself to a doughnut — or even two — without ruining your diet.

WHAT YOU'LL NEED

Mini doughnut pans
2 mixing bowls
Whisk
Ziplock bag
Wire rack

YIELD

28 mini doughnuts

COUNT EACH SERVING AS

1 snack
(Count 2–3 mini doughnuts as a serving, depending on your plan.)

INGREDIENTS

Cooking spray
2 cups white whole wheat flour
1½ teaspoons baking powder
½ teaspoon baking soda
½ teaspoon cinnamon
½ teaspoon salt
½ tablespoon coconut oil
2 teaspoons vanilla extract
1½ teaspoons agave syrup

1 cup unsweetened apple butter
¾ cup unsweetened almond milk

CHOCOLATE GLAZE

2 tablespoons unsweetened cocoa powder
3½ tablespoons unsweetened almond milk
½ teaspoon vanilla extract
6–8 teaspoons zero-calorie sweetener

DIRECTIONS

1   Preheat oven to 350°F. Lightly spray 28 mini doughnut cups with cooking spray.

2   To prepare the doughnuts, whisk together the flour, baking powder, baking soda, cinnamon, and salt in a medium bowl.

3   In a separate bowl, whisk together coconut oil, vanilla, and agave syrup. Stir in the apple butter. Alternate between adding the flour mixture and the almond milk, beginning and ending with the flour mixture, and stirring just until incorporated.

4   Transfer the batter to a large ziplock bag and cut off one corner. Pipe into the prepared doughnut cups. Bake for 12–15 minutes or until the tops are firm to the touch. Cool in the pan for 5 minutes before transferring to a wire rack to cool completely.

5   Prepare the glaze: Stir together the cocoa powder, almond milk, vanilla, and sweetener. Dip each doughnut into the glaze and return to the wire rack or a plate to set.

TREATS AND SNACKS

BLUEBERRY MUFFINS

Try this simple muffin recipe, perfect for a pick-me-up without the extra calories.

INGREDIENTS

½ cup unsweetened applesauce

¼ cup agave syrup

¼ cup canola oil

2 eggs

1 teaspoon vanilla extract

1 cup reduced-fat or fat-free milk or unsweetened almond milk

2⅓ cups + 1 tablespoon white whole wheat flour, divided

1 teaspoon baking soda

1 teaspoon baking powder

¼ cup zero-calorie sweetener

1 cup fresh or frozen blueberries

DIRECTIONS

1   Preheat oven to 350°F. Line a 12-cup muffin pan with paper liners.

2   In a large mixing bowl, whisk together the applesauce, agave syrup, and oil until smooth. Add the eggs and vanilla one at a time, whisking to combine after each addition. Add the milk and whisk until combined.

3   Add 2⅓ cups flour, baking soda, baking powder, and sweetener to the bowl and stir until combined. Do not overmix.

4   In a small bowl, combine the blueberries and remaining 1 tablespoon flour. Stir gently into the muffin batter.

5   Spoon the mixture into the prepared muffin cups, filling each cup about three-quarters full.

6   Bake for 20 minutes, or until a toothpick inserted in the center comes out clean.

LOW-FAT CHOCOLATE CHIP MUFFINS

A lighter version of your favorite treat.

WHAT YOU'LL NEED

Muffin pan
Paper muffin liners
Mixing bowl
Whisk
Blender
Wire rack

YIELD

12 muffins;
1 muffin = 1 serving

COUNT EACH SERVING AS

1 snack

INGREDIENTS

1½ cups whole wheat pastry flour or white whole wheat flour

1 teaspoon baking soda

¼ teaspoon salt

3 bananas

2 tablespoons honey

1 tablespoon vanilla extract

1 tablespoon olive or coconut oil

1 egg

1 tablespoon unsweetened almond milk

½ cup nonfat Greek yogurt or unsweetened applesauce

¼ cup sugar-free chocolate chips (or less)

DIRECTIONS

1 Preheat oven to 350°F. Line a 12-cup muffin pan with paper liners.

2 In a medium bowl, whisk together flour, baking soda, and salt. Place bananas, honey, vanilla, oil, egg, almond milk, and yogurt or applesauce in a blender. Blend on high speed for 1 minute or until well combined, smooth, and creamy.

3 Pour wet ingredients into dry ingredients and mix until just combined. Gently fold in chocolate chips. Divide batter evenly among the muffin cups and bake for 20–25 minutes, or until toothpick comes out clean or with just a few crumbs attached.

4 Cool for 5 minutes, then transfer to a wire rack to finish cooling. Muffins are best served warm and taste even better the next day.

BROWNIE FOR ONE

A most exceptional guilty pleasure without the guilt.

INGREDIENTS

Cooking spray

6 tablespoons zero-calorie sweetener

2 tablespoons white whole wheat flour

2 tablespoons unsweetened cocoa powder

¼ teaspoon baking powder

⅛ teaspoon salt

2 tablespoons unsweetened applesauce

2 egg whites

2 teaspoons unsweetened almond milk

DIRECTIONS

1   Preheat oven to 350°F. Spray a ramekin with cooking spray.

2   Mix sweetener, flour, cocoa powder, baking powder, and salt in a small bowl. Add in applesauce, egg whites, and almond milk and stir until combined.

3   Pour the batter into the ramekin and bake for 8–12 minutes or until toothpick inserted in center comes out clean.

COOKING TIP

For a quick baking cheat, pour the batter into a microwave-safe baking dish and microwave for about 1 minute and 30 seconds.

WHAT YOU'LL NEED

10-ounce ramekin
Mixing bowl

YIELD

1 serving

COUNT EACH SERVING AS

1 treat or 1 snack

FIBER-ONE TREATS

If you don't share with your family, you'll have almost a month's worth of treats in just a few minutes!

INGREDIENTS

1 3.5-ounce dark chocolate bar, 72% cocoa

1 box Original Fiber One Cereal

2 teaspoons reduced-fat peanut butter

DIRECTIONS

1 Line a 9x13-inch baking pan with parchment paper.

2 Break chocolate into pieces and place in a microwave-safe bowl. Melt in 15-second increments, stirring in between, until the chocolate is smooth. Add remaining ingredients and mix well.

3 Pour the mixture into the prepared pan and smooth out so it's even. Let cool, then cut into 24 pieces. Store in a ziplock bag or container in the freezer.

COOKING TIP

Portion control is key here. Try packaging each treat individually so you aren't tempted to eat too many.

WHAT YOU'LL NEED

9x13-inch baking pan

Microwave-safe bowl

YIELD

24 servings

COUNT EACH SERVING AS

1 treat

PEANUT BUTTER CEREAL TREATS

This treat is for all you peanut butter and chocolate lovers out there.

INGREDIENTS

2 cups Rice Krispies or crushed Cheerios

½ cup old-fashioned rolled oats

⅓ cup reduced-fat peanut butter

⅓ cup sugar-free chocolate chips

OPTIONAL ADDITIONS

1 sprinkle wheat germ

1 sprinkle flaxseeds

2 tablespoons slivered almonds

DIRECTIONS

1   Preheat oven to 450°F. Line a 9x13-inch baking pan with parchment paper.

2   Mix together cereal, oats, peanut butter, and chocolate chips, along with any additions desired. Spread in the lined pan and smooth out. Place in oven and bake for 3 minutes.

3   Let cool. Freeze, then cut into 10 bars.

WHAT YOU'LL NEED

9x13-inch baking pan
Mixing bowl

YIELD

10 servings

COUNT EACH SERVING AS

1 treat

PEANUT BUTTER CUPS

Healthy, low calorie, and absolutely delicious!

INGREDIENTS

1 3.5-ounce dark chocolate bar, 72% cocoa

¼ cup unsweetened almond milk, room temperature

1 cup powdered peanut butter

1 cup water

DIRECTIONS

1 Line a mini muffin pan with paper liners and set aside.

2 Place the chocolate in a microwave-safe bowl and microwave at 15-second intervals until fully melted. Gently stir in the almond milk until you have a creamy consistency.

3 Divide the chocolate mixture in half. Distribute one half evenly among the muffin cups. Place the pan in the freezer for a few minutes for the chocolate to solidify.

4 Combine the powdered peanut butter and water until you have a creamy peanut butter texture. (It will be slightly runnier than regular peanut butter, which is fine.)

5 Pour the peanut butter into each muffin cup to create another layer on top of the chocolate. Return the pan to the freezer for about half an hour to allow the peanut butter layer to solidify.

6 Remove the muffin pan from the freezer. Melt the remaining chocolate in the microwave for a few seconds until it reaches a pourable consistency, then pour a thin layer on top of the peanut butter layer in each cup. Return to the freezer until the peanut butter cups are fully frozen.

WHAT YOU'LL NEED

Mini muffin pan

Mini paper muffin liners

Microwave-safe bowl

Mixing bowl

YIELD

10–12 servings

COUNT EACH SERVING AS

1 treat or 1 snack

WHAT YOU'LL NEED

Baking sheet
Large mixing bowl
Airtight container

YIELD

20 servings

COUNT EACH SERVING AS

1 treat

HEALTHY GRANOLA BARS

One batch will provide you with plenty of this healthy and tasty treat, a fantastic alternative to the store-bought variety.

INGREDIENTS

4 cups old-fashioned rolled oats

4 cups brown or regular Rice Krispies

¾–1 cup honey or agave syrup

½ cup oil

1 teaspoon baking soda

½ cup sugar-free chocolate chips

DIRECTIONS

1. Preheat oven to 350°F. Line a baking sheet with parchment paper and set aside.

2. Mix all ingredients in a large bowl. Transfer to the lined baking sheet and smooth down the top. Bake for 20 minutes.

3. Remove the baking sheet from the oven. Using a sharp knife, cut the bars partway through to divide into 20 pieces. Allow the bars to cool and then cut the rest of the way. This will prevent them from crumbling.

4. Store in an airtight container and leave on the counter.

HEALTH TIP

Oats are a great source of important vitamins, minerals, fiber, and more. They've been linked to several health benefits including weight loss, lower blood sugar levels, and a reduced risk of heart disease, among other things.

AVOCADO CHOCOLATE PUDDING

Avocado in chocolate pudding? Who would've thought?! Whoever it was, we're glad they did!

INGREDIENTS

2 ripe avocados

⅓ cup honey

⅓ cup unsweetened cocoa powder

1 teaspoon vanilla extract

½ teaspoon ground chia seeds

DIRECTIONS

1 Blend all ingredients in a blender or food processor until the mixture reaches a smooth consistency.

2 Divide mixture evenly among 10 small cups. Refrigerate for at least 1 hour before serving.

WHAT YOU'LL NEED

Blender or food processor

Small cups

YIELD

10 servings

COUNT EACH SERVING AS

1 treat or 1 fat

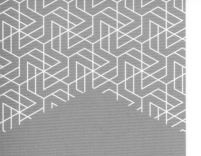

WHAT YOU'LL NEED

Baking sheet

Blender or food processor

YIELD

6 servings

COUNT EACH SERVING AS

1 fruit

PEANUT BUTTER ICE CREAM

Have your ice cream and eat it too with this creamy, frozen treat.

INGREDIENTS

3 large very ripe bananas

1–2 tablespoons unsweetened almond milk, if desired

2 tablespoons powdered peanut butter (you can use the chocolate-flavored powdered peanut butter if desired)

DIRECTIONS

1   Cut the bananas into 1-inch chunks. Arrange banana chunks in a single layer on a large baking sheet. Freeze for at least 4 hours.

2   Place the frozen banana chunks in a blender or food processor and purée until creamy and smooth, scraping down the bowl as necessary. If you have a hard time getting a creamy consistency, you can add 1–2 tablespoons of unsweetened almond milk while blending. Add the powdered peanut butter and purée to combine.

3   Serve immediately for soft-serve ice cream consistency. If you prefer harder ice cream, place in the freezer for a few hours and then serve.

CREAM-STUFFED STRAWBERRIES

A fancy treat to make a dairy dessert yummy and beautiful.

INGREDIENTS

⅓ cup zero-calorie sweetener

4 ounces reduced-fat cream cheese, softened

1 tablespoon amaretto or vanilla extract

16 large strawberries

DIRECTIONS

1   Combine sweetener and softened cream cheese in a bowl and mix well. Add amaretto or vanilla and mix until combined.

2   Cut a small slice off the bottom of each strawberry so it can stand. Using a paring knife, hollow out the berries from the top. Pipe 2 teaspoons cream into each.

🔶 COOKING TIP

If you don't have piping tools, simply use a ziplock sandwich bag and cut off one of the tips.

WHAT YOU'LL NEED

Mixing bowl
Paring knife
Piping tools

YIELD

4 servings

COUNT EACH SERVING AS

1 protein

+

½ fruit

CLASSIC CHEESECAKE

Flavored cheesecake is now a guilt-free pleasure!

INGREDIENTS

1 pound farmer cheese

1 6-ounce container low-fat yogurt, any flavor

2 eggs

⅔ cup zero-calorie sweetener

DIRECTIONS

1   Preheat oven to 350°F.

2   Blend all the ingredients together well. Pour mixture into a 9-inch round baking pan.

3   Place the round pan into a bed of water in the larger pan, making a water bath. Bake for 50–60 minutes. Let cool and refrigerate.

WHAT YOU'LL NEED

Blender or food processor

9-inch round baking pan

Larger baking pan

YIELD

6 servings

COUNT EACH SERVING AS

1 treat or 1 snack

MINI CHERRY CHEESECAKES

The mix of cheese and cherries is brilliantly delicious.

INGREDIENTS

2 eggs, beaten

8 ounces reduced-fat cream cheese

1 cup reduced-fat cottage cheese

¼ cup sugar-free vanilla pudding mix

¼ cup zero-calorie sweetener

1 tablespoon lemon juice

2 teaspoons vanilla extract

1 10-ounce can sugar-free cherry pie filling

DIRECTIONS

1   Preheat oven to 350°F. Line a 12-cup muffin pan with paper liners.

2   Combine all the ingredients except for the cherry pie filling in a blender or food processor. Divide batter among the muffin cups.

3   Bake for 30 minutes, or until set. Refrigerate overnight (or at least 4 hours).

4   Spread cherry pie filling on top just before serving.

WHAT YOU'LL NEED

Muffin pan
Paper muffin liners
Blender or food processor

YIELD

12 mini cheesecakes

COUNT EACH SERVING AS

1 snack

ISRAELI-STYLE CHEESECAKE

The luscious, velvety texture of a rich cheesecake with less fat. Quark cheese, known in Hebrew as gevinah levanah, is commonly found in Israel and now available in America too.

INGREDIENTS

5 egg whites

3 8.8-ounce containers 3% quark cheese

2 tablespoons lite sour cream

4 tablespoons xylitol or your choice of sweetener

½ package sugar-free vanilla pudding mix

3 tablespoons white whole wheat flour

DIRECTIONS

1   Preheat oven to 350°F. Line a 9x13-inch baking pan with parchment paper.

2   In a mixing bowl, beat the egg whites until stiff with a hand mixer. Add the remaining ingredients and mix until you have a smooth consistency. Pour the mixture into the prepared baking pan.

3   Bake uncovered for 1 hour. Remove from oven and let cool before refrigerating.

WHAT YOU'LL NEED

9x13-inch baking pan

Mixing bowl

Hand mixer

YIELD

24 servings

COUNT EACH SERVING AS

1 treat

CHEESE SNACKS

Now you can have your cake and eat it too!

INGREDIENTS

1 pound reduced-fat cottage cheese

1 pound farmer cheese

18 ounces reduced-fat cream cheese

4 eggs

½ cup xylitol or your choice of sweetener

1 teaspoon vanilla extract

DIRECTIONS

1   Preheat oven to 350°F. Line a 12-cup muffin pan with paper liners.

2   Mix all the ingredients together until you have a smooth consistency. Divide the mixture evenly among the lined muffin cups.

3   Bake for 45 minutes. Remove from oven and let cool before refrigerating.

WHAT YOU'LL NEED

Muffin pan
Paper muffin liners
Mixing bowl

YIELD

12 servings

COUNT EACH SERVING AS

1 treat

NECTARINE POPS

These are so tasty and refreshing, perfect for hot weather.

INGREDIENTS

3 large, ripe nectarines

¼ cup orange juice

DIRECTIONS

1   Peel nectarines and cut into chunks.

2   Pour nectarine chunks and orange juice into blender or food processor and blend until just smooth. Freeze in ice pop molds.

WHAT YOU'LL NEED

Blender or food processor

Ice pop mold

YIELD

3 pops

COUNT EACH SERVING AS

1 fruit

DAIRY FRUIT CUPS

This recipe can also be frozen for dairy ice pops. So refreshing!

INGREDIENTS

2 pints hulled strawberries (about 4 cups)

½ cup nonfat Greek yogurt

¼ cup freshly squeezed orange juice

Juice of ½ lemon

2 tablespoons simple syrup or more to taste, made with zero-calorie sweetener (see note)

½ teaspoon vanilla extract

DIRECTIONS

1 Combine strawberries, yogurt, orange and lemon juices, simple syrup, and vanilla in a blender or food processor. Blend until smooth.

2 Divide among 6 cups. Refrigerate until chilled, about 30 minutes.

 NOTE

To make simple syrup, combine 1 part zero-calorie sweetener to 2 parts water in a saucepan. Bring to a simmer, then remove from heat.

Multiply this recipe as needed so you can serve more than one person.

WHAT YOU'LL NEED

Blender or food processor

Cups

YIELD

6 servings

COUNT EACH SERVING AS

1 treat or 1 fruit

BEVERAGES

WHAT YOU'LL NEED

Blender or food processor
Large glass cup

YIELD

1 serving

COUNT EACH SERVING AS

Free

FROZEN CAPPUCCINO

Skip the Starbucks and save the calories!

INGREDIENTS

1 cup black coffee

1 cup ice cubes

Zero-calorie sweetener, to taste

1 tablespoon reduced-fat or fat-free milk

DIRECTIONS

1 Brew your coffee and let cool.

2 Place all the ingredients into a blender or food processor. Blend until smooth and pour into a tall glass. Serve immediately.

🍳 COOKING TIP

Add some garnish such as mint leaves, an orange slice, cinnamon, or instant coffee granules on top for a fancier look and flavor.

SPICED CHAI TEA

Kick back, put your feet up, and relax with this tea after a long day!

INGREDIENTS

8–12 ounces boiling water

1 spiced chai tea bag

4 teaspoons zero-calorie sweetener

1 tablespoon reduced-fat or fat-free milk

DIRECTIONS

1 Place tea bag in a mug with boiling water. Steep for 5 minutes.

2 Discard tea bag and stir in sweetener and milk.

 **COOKING TIP**

You can also pour over ice cubes in a tall glass for a delicious iced chai tea. For some added spice, sprinkle some cinnamon on top, or some instant coffee for a caffeine boost.

WHAT YOU'LL NEED

Mug
Stirrer

YIELD

1 serving

COUNT EACH SERVING AS

Free

ICED COFFEE WITH A KICK

Morning pick-me-up, anyone? How about adding some yummy flavor?

INGREDIENTS

¼ cup boiling water

1 heaping teaspoon instant coffee

1 teaspoon chocolate liqueur

4 teaspoons zero-calorie sweetener,
or to taste

1 cup water

2 ounces reduced-fat or fat-free milk

4 ice cubes

DIRECTIONS

1 Pour the boiling water into a mug or tall glass. Add coffee, liqueur, and sweetener and stir until dissolved.

2 Add 1 cup water, milk, and ice cubes and stir.

COOKING TIP

Lemonade, iced tea, and coffee beverages keep well in the refrigerator for 2–3 days. Prepare ahead for a refreshing, quick pick-me-up. Add the ice cubes immediately before drinking.

WHAT YOU'LL NEED

Mug or tall glass
Coffee stirrer

YIELD

1 serving

COUNT EACH SERVING AS

1 treat

LEMONADE

Perfect as a refreshing drink on a hot summer day!

INGREDIENTS

1 quart water

Juice of 1 lemon

4 teaspoons zero-calorie sweetener

Ice cubes

Lemon slices and mint leaves,
for garnish (optional)

DIRECTIONS

1 Place 1 quart of water into a pitcher. Add lemon juice. Stir in sweetener. Add ice as desired.

2 Garnish with lemon slices and mint leaves, if desired, and serve in a tall glass.

COOKING TIP

Scoop the pulp out of the lemon and blend slightly so the pulp is finer. Stir into the pitcher for lemonade with pulp.

WHAT YOU'LL NEED

Pitcher
Large glass cup
Stirrer

YIELD

4 servings

COUNT EACH SERVING AS

Free

STRAWBERRY LIMEADE

Picture yourself on a tropical island with this in your hand... Aaahhh!

WHAT YOU'LL NEED

Pitcher
Large glass
Stirrer

YIELD

4 servings

COUNT EACH SERVING AS

Free

INGREDIENTS

1 quart water

Juice of 1 lime

4 teaspoons zero-calorie sweetener

Crushed ice

1 strawberry, sliced

DIRECTIONS

1   Place 1 quart of water into a pitcher. Add the lime juice to the pitcher along with the sweetener.

2   Add ice as desired.

3   Garnish with sliced strawberries, or mash the strawberry and mix it in to add flavor and color.

COOKING TIP

Replace the lime with lemons, oranges, or grapefruits for more flavor variety.

SPARKLING FRUIT JELLO

This is guaranteed to be the hit of any party, so be sure to make plenty!

INGREDIENTS

3 cups boiling water

2 packages sugar-free Jello

5 cups cold seltzer

1 11-ounce can mandarin oranges, drained

½ cup sliced strawberries

½ cup seedless grapes, halved

1 kiwi, sliced

DIRECTIONS

1   In a large bowl, stir the boiling water into the Jello mix for at least 2 minutes until completely dissolved. Refrigerate for 15 minutes. Gently stir in seltzer.

2   Pour into a clear 2½-quart glass punch bowl and cover.

3   For extra sparkling bubbles, refrigerate for 15 minutes, then gently stir for 5 seconds.

4   Refrigerate for 4 hours or until firm. Top with fruit just before serving.

WHAT YOU'LL NEED

Large bowl
Punch bowl

YIELD

4 servings

COUNT EACH SERVING AS

1 fruit on Shabbos (or leave out the fruit and count as free)

COUNT 2 SERVINGS AS

1 treat

STRAWBERRY SORBET SMOOTHIE

For some tropical flavor on a hot day, have this delicious smoothie.

INGREDIENTS

1 cup frozen strawberries

1 cup ice cubes

2 teaspoons zero-calorie sweetener

DIRECTIONS

1   Allow the strawberries to defrost partially so they're still semi-frozen.

2   Place all ingredients into a blender or food processor. Blend until smooth and pour into a tall glass with a straw. If the mixture is too thick, add some water to thin. Serve immediately.

 COOKING TIP

For a variety, use 1 medium orange, segmented, in place of the strawberries.

WHAT YOU'LL NEED

Blender or food processor
Large cup
Straw

YIELD

1 serving

COUNT EACH SERVING AS

1 fruit

CHOCOLATE PEANUT BUTTER MILKSHAKE

A rich and filling milkshake to satisfy your sweet tooth.

INGREDIENTS

1 cup unsweetened almond milk

1 cup ice cubes

2 teaspoons unsweetened cocoa powder

2 tablespoons powdered peanut butter

1 teaspoon (5 drops) stevia or your choice of sweetener, or to taste

Dash sea salt

DIRECTIONS

1   Place all ingredients into a blender or food processor. Blend until well combined and frothy.

2   Pour into a glass and enjoy.

WHAT YOU'LL NEED

Blender or food processor

Glass

YIELD

1 serving

COUNT EACH SERVING AS

1 snack

The tasty, healthy way to detox.

INGREDIENTS

⅔ cup unsweetened almond milk

¾ cup ice cubes

1½ cups kale or other green leafy vegetables, chopped

1 stalk celery, chopped

½ green apple, cored and chopped

1 tablespoon ground flaxseed

1 teaspoon honey (optional)

DIRECTIONS

1   Combine all ingredients in a blender or food processor. Blend until smooth.

2   Pour into a glass and enjoy.

WHAT YOU'LL NEED

Blender or food processor
Tall glass

YIELD

1 serving

COUNT EACH SERVING AS

1 snack

INDEX